'I was once married to a very handsome man.'

Laura smiled tightly. 'Like you, he didn't consider a commitment to one woman any reason not to pursue others.'

The line of Mike's mouth thinned. 'Still as forthright as ever, Ms Maxwell. Do you intend to go on forever tarring any man who isn't ugly with that same brush?'

'Let me tell you, Mr Wonderful Brady, that it takes more than good looks and charm to—'

He grinned suddenly. 'So you have noticed?'

Dear Reader

There's something different about Mills & Boon romances! From now on, in the front pages of all our stories, you'll find a short extract to tempt you to read on, a biography about the author and a letter from the editor, all of which we hope will welcome you to our heart-warming world of romance. What's more, if you've got any comments or suggestions to make about Mills & Boon's stories, drop us a line; we'll be glad to hear from you.

See you next month!

The Editor

Shirley Kemp was born in South Wales, but has the blood of all four countries of Great Britain in her veins. That probably explains her infuriatingly impulsive and restless personality, which has recently taken her off to live in France.

She was second eldest in a family of seven children, and spare time was rare, but she read voraciously and wrote for enjoyment.

Writing romantic fiction is a natural extension of that youthful pursuit and she still enjoys it just as much.

DENIAL OF LOVE

BY

SHIRLEY KEMP

M I L L S & B O O N L I M I T E D
ETON HOUSE 18-24 PARADISE ROAD
RICHMOND SURREY TW9 1SR

First published in Great Britain 1992
by Mills & Boon Limited

This edition 1992

ISBN 0 263 77544 5

Set in Times Roman 10½ on 12 pt.
01-9205-49469 C

Made and printed in Great Britain

CHAPTER ONE

LAURA MAXWELL tripped over the pile of letters on the hall carpet and bent to retrieve them just as the telephone rang.

The sound of the bell ringing so close to her ear made her start, and it was as much as she could do to contain her irritation when she heard the voice on the other end of the telephone.

'Laura. Is that you, dear?'

'Mother, of course it's me. Who else would it be?'

'Don't be cross, dear.' Her mother's injured tone made her feel guilty. 'I just wanted to remind you about Thursday. You did say you'd take the day off to try on your wedding dress.'

Laura stifled a sigh. A completely wasted day as far as she was concerned, since her wedding was more than two months away, and she'd already tried on her gown twice, and her mother was still dissatisfied.

Besides which, it seemed to Laura a little ridiculous to be getting married for the second time in lavish white with all the trimmings, especially with a four-year-old son as her page boy. But her mother had been adamant and, although Laura normally stood her ground pretty firmly, she had to concede that in this, her first *real* wedding, she owed Florence some concession.

'I haven't forgotten Thursday,' Laura said now, 'and I promise I'll be there. Now I must hurry. I've got someone coming.'

'But dear, I haven't finished discussing——'

'We'll discuss it when I see you,' Laura cut in firmly. 'Bye.'

She could feel her mother's outrage crackling along the line as she returned the receiver to its rest. But there was no time to wrestle with her conscience now. There was a design sketch to be completed for a client before the end of the week, and in less than an hour there would be a new client at her door.

She hadn't met Mike Brady, but he was a good friend of Brian Huxley and, according to Brian, money would be no object in the interior design of the large country house he had recently acquired.

She showered quickly and went into the bedroom to dress and make-up. She always dressed with care. Not out of the kind of pride her mother exhibited so appallingly, but because, to her clients, she was her own shop window.

She stared fixedly at her reflection in the dressing-table mirror, studying the tell-tale smudges beneath her unusual hazel-green eyes with gloomy intensity. The bright copper tones of her long, thick hair seemed to lack its usual lustre and her jaundiced eye refused to see the beauty of her flawless honeyed skin and the allure of her wide and sensitive mouth.

'God! I look like death,' she groaned contemptuously.

This wedding was beginning to take its toll of her looks, not to mention her patience and energy, coming at a time when her one-man interior design business was suddenly taking an upward swing. Satisfied clients were beginning to circulate the news, and if orders continued to flow in at the same pace she would soon have to think about taking a partner to help her cope.

Last week had been hectic, and the next two months, ending with the wedding, would be frantic, and now here was her mother taking up more of her time than was necessary in her search for perfection. She had just finished brushing her hair when the doorbell rang. With a last searching look at her reflection, she went to answer it.

As she opened the door, she came face to face with the most devastating man she had ever set eyes on, and in those first timeless seconds she imprinted on her mind every minute detail of his appearance.

He was tall, loose-limbed and powerfully built, yet with an air of lean toughness that attracted her immediately. This man, in his neat, conservative suit, emanated a strong animal vitality which was undeniable, and which drew Laura unwillingly like metal to a magnet.

His rich brown hair, which grew in thick abundance to fall nonchalantly over his broad forehead, shone, burnished by the morning sun to russet. Thick dark brows arched above brilliant summer-blue eyes, which softened the harshness of the granite-hewn face.

'Good morning,' he said pointedly as she continued to stare at him in speechless surprise. 'My name is Mike Brady.'

'I . . . I thought it . . . might be,' she said faintly.

He frowned impatiently as she continued to stare at him. 'Am I allowed to come in?'

Brought back to earth, Laura flushed crimson. 'Yes. Yes, of course.' She stood back to let him enter, and he turned to face her in the hallway.

Never in her life had she been so bowled over by a man, and he was obviously aware of the fact. His summer-blue eyes glinted into hers, his expression strangely wary, as though he was awaiting some particular response from her.

'Won't you come through?' Laura's professional poise hadn't entirely deserted her, but her knees were definitely buckling as she led him into her office-cum-studio.

'You seem a little put out, Ms Maxwell,' he said calmly, as he seated himself on the opposite side of her small desk. 'Weren't you expecting me?'

'Yes, of course I was.' Laura drew a calming breath. 'And I'm looking forward to hearing your plans,' she went on, steering him adroitly into the channels where she felt most at ease. 'From what Brian told me they're going to be a real challenge.'

Brian Huxley was a merchant banker for whom she'd recently redecorated an entire flat. A bachelor, he'd been delighted with the cunningly homely effect she'd managed to impart to the completely male décor she'd designed for him.

'Are you also a bachelor, Mr Brady?'

'Yes. For the moment. But I intend to marry quite soon.'

The sardonic lift of his dark brows had her blushing like a schoolgirl. The query had been purely in the interests of understanding the kind of job she would have to deal with, of course, but from his look he had apparently put a wholly different connotation on it. His conceit annoyed her, and she found herself wanting to put him down.

'How nice,' she said coolly. 'I'm getting married myself in just over two months, which is why I intend pushing full steam ahead on your interior designs.'

He frowned in what seemed like deep annoyance, and there was a pause before he went on. 'My congratulations. But are you sure you'll manage in that short time?'

Laura bit her lip, wondering why she found it so difficult to be absolutely professional with him. He hadn't had to be informed of her wedding plans. She'd told him out of pure pique—an emotion she didn't experience very often.

'I'm sure,' she said hastily. 'And I assure you I'll give your work my undivided attention. I won't disappoint you.'

His bright blue eyes flicked over her with practised ease. 'No. I don't think you could ever do that.'

Laura flushed. For a moment, she'd read something quite different into his words, and her hackles rose. Why did men always have to bring sex into everything? But wasn't that what you were doing a little while ago? a sneaky little voice spoke inside her head. You were ogling him quite blatantly. It serves you right if he's now trying to take you up on it.

But it was more than that. Somehow, she couldn't shake off a feeling that there was something he was expecting of her...if only she could work out what it was.

'I'm glad to have your confidence, Mr Brady,' she said, coolly efficient. 'So let's get down to business right away.' She caught his eye deliberately, daring him to misinterpret that, but his expression was solemn.

'That's why I came here, Ms Maxwell. I'm always ready to talk business.'

And his business was, thankfully, completely engrossing. She found herself becoming more and more excited by the outline he was giving her.

He had recently purchased a large country house and, since he was intending, in the near future, to marry, its interior design would have to cater for the separate and yet combined needs and tastes of a family, from a nursery suite to his own retreat of a study. At the end of the discussion, Laura felt elated. It was a project she knew she was going to enjoy.

She cut her mind off firmly as it began to speculate about the kind of woman with whom he would choose to share the fruits of her labour. A brainless blonde with a beautiful face and a film-star figure? she conjectured sourly, and then wondered sardonically if he would be able to stand the competition.

'When can you come out to see the place?'

The question, natural enough in the circumstances, unexpectedly set her pulses racing. 'I . . . I'll have to take a look at my diary,' she said, and silently cursed her fingers, which seemed strangely to have become all thumbs as she turned the pages.

'I could manage Friday morning,' she said at last. 'If you can arrange for me to have the keys?'

When he smiled a fascinating fold appeared in both cheeks, Laura noted almost absently, and then wondered why her insides seemed to have caught fire.

'That won't be necessary. I'll pick you up and take you there myself.'

'Ah!' Laura said warily. 'That's kind, but I usually manage better on my own.'

'Perhaps.' He nodded coolly. 'Nevertheless, I do have one or two preferences that I think I should make you aware of before you start.'

Laura frowned. Most of her clients were only too happy to let her have a free hand with her designs. After all, it was her expertise they were paying for. She hoped Mike Brady wouldn't prove to be one of the few who made life awkward for her.

'Well, if you insist, of course I'll listen, but I think I should point out that there's a very fine line between acceptable preference and interference.'

He snorted impatiently. 'I hope you intend to be reasonable, Ms Maxwell. After all, I do have to live in the place.'

She saw the sardonic lift of his brows and flushed a little before going on. 'Agreed. But, perhaps, if your preferences are very strong, you should go the whole way and design the entire interior yourself.'

He gave her a cold, steady look. 'If I thought I could do that, Ms Maxwell, I would hardly be wasting my time offering the job to you.' He waved a dismissive hand. 'Of course, if you don't wish to take it...'

Laura bit her lip, wondering why he made her feel so antagonistic. Perhaps it had something to do with his good looks. Ricky had been her inoculation against handsome men like Mike Brady, and she normally gave them a wide berth, but the job he was offering was too good to miss for the sake of a little prejudice.

It would be no use to argue, that was obvious. Laura knew instinctively that here was a man used to getting what he wanted without argument. Her spine stiffened. She tried always to give her clients the best possible results, but she doubted whether that would be possible if he was going to hang about her the whole time. She was tempted to have it out with him now, to put his determination to the test—but paused to consider. Her position might be stronger once the job was actually under way, and by then she might have a better assessment of his character and be able to judge her moves more carefully.

'Very well,' she said a little stiffly. 'If you could pick me up here at ten o'clock on Friday?'

A triumphant little smile curved his lips, and Laura found herself curling her fingers angrily into her palm. The first move in the game was his, but she was damned if she'd allow him such an easy victory the next time!

'It will be my pleasure,' he said, and his expression left her in no doubt that he knew she was fighting her temper.

He left five minutes later, but for the rest of the afternoon Laura found it unusually difficult to put her mind to her work. His handsome face kept intervening between her mind's eye and the paper on which she was attempting to work.

It was hard to say why he'd had such a disconcerting effect on her. It was more than just his good looks. There was a strength of purpose about him that let her know he would make a powerful adversary. And she was back to speculating. If a man like that fell in love...

She caught herself up with a start, aghast at the melting sensations of her insides, and gave herself a mental shake. If this was pre-wedding nerves, it was something she could well do without. Perhaps she should take some aspirin. But she knew aspirin wasn't the answer, and a shudder ran tinglingly through the length of her body as she remembered he was coming to pick her up at ten o'clock on Friday morning.

In the event, Laura saw Mike Brady before then.

On Tuesday afternoon, Brian Huxley telephoned her. 'Laura!' he cried enthusiastically. 'I thought I'd better remind you about my flat-warming tomorrow night. I can't have the guest of honour forgetting to turn up.'

Laura hid a groan. As a matter of fact, the party had slipped to the back of her mind. Probably a Freudian slip, since she hadn't been too keen on the nomination of guest of honour in the first place.

'Of course I haven't forgotten,' she told him, adding a little warily, 'but I would like you to promise you won't go overboard in singing my praises. You know how it makes me squirm.'

'Nonsense!' Brian swept aside her reservations. 'You deserve every bit. And there are one or two people coming who've already expressed themselves very interested in your work. They're looking forward to seeing you.'

Laura felt a surge of warmth. He really did try very hard on her behalf. 'Bless you, Brian. You're a gem.'

If she hadn't been too busy to give it any deep thought, she might have guessed Mike Brady would be there. She saw him almost at once, standing in a corner talking to Brian. But he didn't cross the room with Brian as he came to greet her.

Laura found herself sighing with relief. Just the unexpected sight of him had her insides fluttering with unaccustomed nervousness and she hoped she would have time to compose herself before being faced with the task of talking to him.

She wished, suddenly, that Hubert had agreed to bring her. He wasn't comfortable in social gatherings where the guests were total strangers to him, so she really hadn't expected him to accompany her. The most she had been able to wring out of him was a promise that he would pick her up at about ten o'clock to take her home.

After the embarrassment of being hailed as guest of honour, and the inevitable introductions and small talk with Brian's guests, she began to relax. Mike Brady had made no move to seek her out. He seemed quite happy with the company of a tall redhead, who was vaguely familiar.

One of the guests pointed her out later as Marietta Strang, a young actress, who was currently appearing in a TV advertisement for chocolate.

'Don't they make a lovely couple?' a middle-aged woman commented, following Laura's curious gaze.

'Yes,' Laura admitted, with a strange little twinge. 'Is that the girl he is going to marry?'

The woman's eyes widened and then narrowed delightedly. 'I don't know for sure, of course, but I shouldn't be a bit surprised.'

'Neither should I!' Laura muttered beneath her breath, studying the girl's lovely face and slim form. It seemed hardly designed for motherhood, she thought critically, and especially not the large brood Mike Brady had hinted at.

Oh, well. She supposed he knew his own business best, and at least it would mean that his attention would be occupied with his beautiful companion, though what danger he might have represented alone she was unable to define.

'She's a lucky girl,' the woman continued. 'Their house will obviously be a dream, with the whole of Designers' Choice to choose from.'

Laura frowned, remembering that it had indeed been one of the preferences Mike Brady had mentioned to her in their discussion—that she make all the choices of furnishings and fabrics, wall-coverings and so on from the ranges of Designers' Choice. She had to admit that she'd been impressed at the time. Designers' Choice was one of the most exclusive chains of shops and, arguably, the most expensive.

'I imagine his pocket will stand the strain,' she said with an edge of cynicism in her voice.

The woman laughed. 'It won't be that much of a strain, my dear. He owns the company.'

Laura's mouth dropped open. 'Mike Brady owns Designers' Choice?'

'But of course.' Pale brows rose a little condescendingly. 'I thought everyone knew that.'

Well, I didn't, Laura thought to herself a little resentfully. I wonder why he didn't see the need to tell me?

Not that it would have mattered, but, as the news sank in, she couldn't help wondering why he had chosen her to do his interior designs for Gladstone House, when he would probably have any number of established designers virtually at his beck and call?

It looked as though Brian Huxley had pulled some very powerful strings on her behalf after all. Perhaps Mike Brady owed Brian a favour, she thought in an attempt at humour. Well, it would have to be a pretty big favour, she added a little grimly, to get him to take on a relative unknown like herself.

Maybe that was why Mike Brady's face had brought such a strong sense of *déjà vu*. After all, as he was owner of such an illustrious company, she was bound to have seen photographs of him somewhere at some time.

Laura didn't actually come face to face with Mike Brady until they met at the buffet table. He was standing on the opposite side, so she could hardly pretend she hadn't seen him.

'Good evening, Ms Maxwell,' he said politely. 'I hope you're enjoying the party?'

'Yes, thanks. Very much.' Laura's gaze skirted away from his. There was a faintly mocking gleam in his eyes which she found difficult to meet. Somehow, the food she was attempting to put on her plate eluded her and crumbled back on to the serving dish. Almost before she knew it, he was beside her.

'Allow me.'

Before she had time to protest, he had taken her plate from her strangely nerveless fingers and began placing some of the most appetising pieces on to it.

'That's more than enough,' she cut in hastily, as he seemed about to pile it up. 'I'm not really that hungry.'

'Slimming?' He eyed her quizzically as he handed her her plate. 'Surely not.'

He appraised her candidly, bringing the colour stinging into her cheeks. His expression seemed to tell her that he liked what he saw. She guessed it was a look he practised all the time—part of his repertoire with women. And, of course, with his striking good looks, there would always be plenty of women.

'No. I really don't have time to worry about my weight.'

He nodded solemnly. 'That's because you don't have to. You're in perfect shape.'

'Thank you,' Laura gritted tightly, as his gaze swept over her again. She would have moved away, but he had hold of her elbow and was leading her to a vacant corner.

'I hope your—er—fiancé...' he paused on the word as though it was distasteful '...I hope he appreciates his...luck.' Again, that hesitation, which, for some reason, had Laura fuming.

'I'm sure he does,' she said icily. 'Which is more than I can say for your—er—fiancée. Judging by her expression, I imagine she feels anything but lucky at the moment. Have you perhaps forgotten to bring her her food?' She nodded across to where Marietta Strang was sitting, with an empty seat beside her, one long slim leg crossed over the other and swinging irritably.

'You mean Marietta?' He shook his head. 'No. I don't think so. Unlike you, Marietta seems to be on a permanent diet, which probably accounts for her irritable temper, as well as her rather spare lines.' His amused blue eyes were back on Laura, following her shapely curves. 'It's a pleasure to see a woman enjoying her food, instead of picking at it like a fussy bird.'

Laura, who had indeed been enjoying the tasty bite-sized delicacies he had chosen for her from the buffet, suddenly lost her appetite. Was he implying she'd been making a pig of herself?

'Well, I think Brian is trying to attract my attention,' she said with a sense of relief as she caught sight of his impatiently waving hand.

'Yes. And that's Judge Barnett he's with.' Mike Brady's mouth curled a little at one corner. 'He's probably being lined up for you as another potential client.'

Laura's eyes flew back to his, trying to read his expression, but it was perfectly bland.

'Is that what happened to you?' she said a little sharply. 'Is that why you chose to be my client, when you probably have any number of your own designers within Designers' Choice?'

He seemed amused by the hint of indignation in her voice, and a cool little smile played at the corners of his mouth. 'I had my reasons,' he said succinctly. 'Let's just say I was looking for a fresh new viewpoint.'

Laura frowned, still not convinced. 'How do you know you will get it from me?'

'Oh, I usually get what I want, Ms Maxwell . . . in the end . . .'

There was something about the way he said that, and the gleam in his blue eyes, that made her feel uneasy as well as annoyed.

'It must be wonderful to be so sure of yourself,' she flashed.

That tantalising fold appeared again in his cheek. 'Sizing people up is part of my stock in trade, Ms Maxwell,' he replied enigmatically. 'A kind of sixth sense about people is what accounts for at least half of my success.'

Laura wondered why his answer had her trembling faintly, as she made her way through the other guests to where Brian was still waving at her. She willed herself not to turn to see whether Mike Brady had gone back to Marietta.

Later, someone cleared a space in the centre of the room and couples began to dance. Laura groaned. All the smiling and small talk had left her drained. The last thing she wanted now was to have her toes trodden on by an unknown dancing partner. She wished she didn't have to wait until Hubert arrived. If he hadn't been coming to pick her up, she might have been able to slip away unnoticed.

She looked fretfully at her watch. Nine-thirty—another half an hour to wait. She sighed.

'Bored, Ms Maxwell?' A deep voice spoke almost directly into her ear. Startled and indignant, she turned to look into Mike Brady's handsome face.

'Did you have to creep up on me like that?' she demanded tightly, listening to the loud thud of her heart against her ribs, and wondering how much of it was due to the fright he'd given her.

He laughed shortly. 'I could hardly make my approach heard above the present din.' He looked calmly into her aggravated face. 'I didn't think you were the nervous type.'

'You're quite right. I'm not,' she denied shortly. 'But it's been a long day and an eventful evening . . .'

'And what you'd really like is to go home,' he finished for her.

She relented a little, giving him a rueful smile. 'You're right about that too.'

'Then allow me to escort you.'

He had his hand about her shoulder, already beginning to steer her towards the hall door, but she resisted him.

'Thank you, but that won't be necessary. Someone is coming to pick me up shortly.'

'Ah.' His eyes glinted, but he didn't relinquish his hold on her. 'The prospective groom, I presume?'

It was almost a pun, and Laura bristled. 'Right yet again, Mr Brady,' she said cynically. 'Doesn't that sixth sense of yours ever let you down?'

He shrugged easily, refusing to be drawn by her anger. 'Hardly ever, I'm pleased to say.'

Laura bit back a sarcastic retort about swollen heads which was threatening to burst past her lips. She had to remind herself that he was, after all, a prospective client, and developing an argument with him was hardly the way to begin a successful business relationship.

His hand had, somehow, slipped from her shoulders to her waist, and he drew her to his side. 'Well, since you have a little time to kill, would you like to dance?'

'I don't think——' Laura's protest was lost in the general hubbub, as he led her to the makeshift dance floor.

Someone had turned down the lights, and in the shadows Mike Brady's face seemed unnervingly mysterious. Without speaking, he drew her against him and, as she hesitated, he took her hands and placed them on his shoulders.

'Relax,' he commanded. 'I hardly ever bite.'

Physically he might not, she thought grimly, but his personality certainly did.

Within the circle of his arms, Laura was strongly aware of him. His shoulders were powerfully muscled, the wall of his chest hard against the softness of her breasts. His hold on her was firm but not tight, and the brush of his body against hers as they moved slowly to the music produced, Laura found to her consternation, an electric excitement.

As she looked up, he caught her in his gaze, the brightness of his blue eyes muted in the dim light to deep, alluring grey. She gazed back at him, with that same tantalising feeling of *déjà vu*, as though she'd looked into those eyes countless times before, which was ridiculous. Or was it?

'Have we met before, Mr Brady?' she asked suddenly.

His dark brows rose. 'Not a very original line, but it's a start.'

Laura frowned irritably. 'Could we dispense with the usual party gambits? I really do feel as though I've seen you somewhere in the past.'

'Interesting,' he said solemnly. 'But you can't remember where. Was it a happy encounter?'

A strong chord was struck deep within, but the memory refused to surface. She shook her head in annoyance. 'I don't know, but I'll make the connection sooner or later.'

He brought his head close to hers, his lips lightly brushing against her temple. 'Let me know when it happens. It could be important.'

Laura pulled back slightly, not liking the giddy sensations his nearness produced. He looked down at her, but she avoided those compelling eyes. 'I shouldn't think we've met, or else I wouldn't have forgotten quite so thoroughly.'

'Was that a compliment?' he said, with mock incredulity.

'Not exactly.' Laura cursed her careless tongue. 'I just happen to have a very retentive memory.'

He laughed softly. 'In that case, our meeting . . . if meet we did . . . was perhaps too disturbing to remember.'

Laura felt a peculiar jolt. Was he trying to tell her something? Give her a clue? She made an impatient sound. 'I'm afraid that's just a little too complex for me at this time of the night, Mr Brady.'

'Then let's forget it and enjoy the dance.' He drew her closer, his cheek resting against her hair. He moved easily and rhythmically and, despite herself, Laura couldn't help but feel the magic he was creating. She closed her eyes and felt her body softening against his.

She was brought back to earth by a curt tap on her shoulder.

'Have I come too early, Laura?' Hubert's voice, clipped with annoyance, broke the spell.

Guiltily, she tried to spring away from Mike Brady, but he released her slowly and with obvious reluctance. Strangely, she could feel the same tremor in him as was reverberating through her own body, as though she'd just been jolted out of a dream. He seemed to recover quickly.

'Ah! Your escort has arrived,' he remarked pleasantly. 'So I'll let you go.' Outrageously, he raised her hand to his lips. 'But don't forget our appointment on Friday.'

'Thank you, Mr Brady,' Laura said stiffly. Her face flamed crimson with an inexplicable fury at the subtle implication his words conveyed. The baiting was obviously deliberate. 'And of course I won't forget.'

She had allowed herself to get carried away, so it was unfair to blame him entirely, but she couldn't rid herself of the feeling that he was playing some kind of personal game. She turned to Hubert, whose face was growing more thunderous by the second.

'Let me introduce you to my fiancé, Hubert Laine,' she said hastily to Mike Brady—and to Hubert. 'Mr Brady is a client. I'm going to redesign the interior of his newly acquired house.'

'How interesting.' Hubert, who was normally the epitome of good manners, shook Mike Brady's proffered hand as though it might bite and then turned pointedly away. He took her arm firmly. 'If I'd known my prompt arrival would spoil your enjoyment,' he said testily, 'I might have delayed it.'

'Don't be ridiculous, Hubert,' she responded through a thin smile which she pinned to her face for the benefit of onlookers. He led her away, and she didn't dare look back for fear of what she might see in Mike Brady's eyes. She felt a smouldering anger that exploded as soon as she and Hubert were in the car.

'How dare you behave like that in front of an important client—as though you were a Victorian father recovering his wayward daughter from the brink of an indiscretion?'

Hubert's face, which had been the colour of boiled lobster, now looked disconcertingly pale. 'And that's precisely what you appear to be sometimes, Laura,' he said in a tightly controlled voice. 'Do you behave that way with all your clients?'

'What way?' Laura glared. 'We were dancing. People usually do at parties.'

She couldn't help a small stab of guilt as she remembered the sensations she had been experiencing in Mike Brady's arms, but that wasn't the point at issue here. This was all about personal and professional freedom.

'I'm only concerned with you,' he insisted stubbornly. 'As my future wife, I think you owe it to me to behave decently in public.'

'Are you saying I was indecent?' she challenged him furiously.

He shot her a frowning look. 'There are certain standards, Laura.'

'Indeed! Well, perhaps your standards and mine don't coincide as closely as I thought.'

'Perhaps,' he agreed coldly. 'But I hardly think this is the time or place to discuss it.'

'You could be right,' Laura bit back, pausing suddenly as she realised this was the nearest they'd ever come to quarrelling—and it was all because of Mike Brady.

She took a deep breath. Hubert was right. Now wasn't the right time to pursue the matter. They were both angry, and it might be better to wait until they could both think more logically, when she was sure she would be able to point out to Hubert the unreasonableness of his attitude.

Hubert left her, rather abruptly, at the door of her flat. He pecked absently at her cheek, and Laura sighed. He was obviously still sulking. And she had a low tolerance for that kind of behaviour in an adult, she admitted mournfully, as she tossed and turned restlessly in her bed.

She'd had a severe jolting tonight, in more ways than one.

Hubert's emergence as an almost Victorian tyrant had shaken her thoroughly, but she was almost equally disconcerted by her own physical reactions to Mike Brady's undeniable animal magnetism. She tried to reassure herself that both phenomena were the result of the tensions of the coming wedding, but her reasoning wasn't entirely successful.

CHAPTER TWO

ANNOYINGLY, it was the question of where, when, or if at all she had met Mike Brady in the past that had kept Laura awake the longest.

Standing on a footstool in her mother's bedroom the following day, she was still thinking of him and still asking herself the same question, without finding an answer.

She stared fixedly at her reflection in the long, oval mirror, her gaze travelling down the column of her throat and on to where the white satin gown stretched tightly across her firm bosom, sweeping down to fit neatly at her narrow waist. It was a beautiful, if somewhat fussy dress, and she wished disconsolately that she could raise a little more enthusiasm for it. The lacy white veil on her head, despite its expensive beauty, only added to her pallor, giving her an unnatural ethereal look.

She sighed deeply, and her mother, kneeling at her feet to adjust the hem, looked up enquiringly.

'I'm sorry, Mother,' Laura said. 'But I'm just not in the mood for trying on a wedding gown.'

Florence Maxwell rose stiffly from her knees. 'This isn't *a* wedding gown, Laura, it's *your* wedding gown, and I intend to make sure it fits you properly.'

Laura made an impatient sound. 'Mother! It's perfect as it is.' She swept her slim hands over the silky folds at her hips. 'There's no way you can improve on it, and I just wish you'd stop trying. Poor Mrs Brinson must be fed up with the whole thing.'

Florence bristled. 'Mrs Brinson is being paid a small fortune, so she'll just have to go on being fed up until she gets it right.' She made an exasperated sound. 'I want this to be the kind of wedding you should have had in the first place. If you hadn't run off——'

'OK! OK!' Laura cut in irritably. 'Let's not go over all that again. I admit marrying Ricky was a mistake. He was a wonderfully good-looking man and I thought I was in love. That was a mistake too, but I don't intend to go on paying for it forever.'

She'd thought herself madly in love with Ricky Daye, a film stunt man, and her elopement with him had seemed very romantic at the time, but she'd soon been disillusioned. There had been nothing romantic about their sparsely furnished flat, where she'd waited alone, often for days, for him to come back off location. His death, in a stunt which went tragically wrong, had left her with a two-year-old son to care for and a strong determination never again to be swayed by a handsome face.

'Yes. Well,' Florence muttered grudgingly. 'Perhaps we should just be grateful for Hubert.'

'Yes,' Laura said firmly. 'Perhaps we should.'

But the mention of Hubert had brought back the events of last night, which had created a loose end it was essential to tie, but she wasn't yet ready to think about that.

Annoyingly, Mike Brady's face popped once more into her mind's eye. Today, it seemed, all avenues of thought led inevitably to him. That lean, intelligent face and the combination of rich brown hair and blue,

blue eyes was absolutely compelling . . . and there was something engaging about that faint tilt of his head...

She caught herself up as some memory stirred. She held her breath and waited, but annoyingly it slipped away. She licked lips that seemed suddenly to have gone very dry. 'Mother, can we stop for a while? I'm just dying for a cup of tea.'

'Tea?' Florence looked up at her daughter, her cool eyes wide in disbelief. 'You want to drink tea... wearing your wedding dress? Don't be foolish, Laura. You can't risk staining it now.'

Laura gave a short impatient laugh. 'Then the solution is simple. I'll take it off. But I've got to have a cup of tea.'

'But I haven't finished.'

Laura's patience suddenly snapped. 'As far as I'm concerned, this gown is as finished now as it's ever going to be,' she erupted. 'This is the last time I'll wear the damned thing until such time as I have to...to get to the altar!'

'Laura!' Her mother was outraged. 'How can any bride curse her wedding gown that way?'

'Easily.' Laura gritted her teeth. 'Especially when it's been thrust on her as often as this one has on me.' She shook her head as her mother seemed about to launch into another argument. 'Tea, Mother!' She set her lips grimly. 'Or I may be tempted to go call the whole thing off.'

Florence eyed her in consternation. 'That joke is in very bad taste, Laura.'

'It's no joke, believe me.' She slipped out of the gown and petticoats and hung them up carefully while an unexpectedly subdued Florence went to arrange for the tea.

Laura dressed and went downstairs to see Joe. Because so much of her time had been taken up initially in building the business, and she'd often worked late into the evening, it had seemed better that her young son should stay with her parents during the week, coming home to her at the flat at the weekend. It was a temporary measure that Laura increasingly had come to see as a potential disaster, since it put Joe's still pliant personality into danger of being overwhelmed by Florence.

When she was married, she would be able to think more positively about taking a partner to share the load. She would be able then to take only the jobs which gave her the most satisfaction, and that would enable her to make the necessary time to be with her son.

'I'll be out on the terrace, Mother,' she called as she bypassed the kitchen.

Joe was there, sitting on her father's lap, listening, solemn-faced, to the story his grandfather was unfolding. She sighed. In her eagerness to get Joe away, out of reach of her mother's inhibitive brand of education, she'd neglected to consider her father. It was suddenly obvious that, in the beginning at least, her little son was going to miss the absorbed attention of the only male figure he'd ever really known in his life.

And that was one of the factors she had taken into consideration when accepting Hubert's proposal of marriage. It would put a male figure back into Joe's life. She and Hubert had never actually discussed having a family, but Laura suspected he wouldn't be happy with a house full of children, so it was just as well she only had the one.

Unlike Mike Brady!

She sighed again. He was back once more to haunt her. A man of obvious passion, already planning ahead for the anticipated fruits of that passion. He wanted children...lots of them, he'd told her, straight-faced...and some poor woman was destined to be the vessel of his ambition. If Marietta Strang really was his intended bride, he might have to adapt that ambition a little more realistically, she thought sardonically.

A mental picture, startlingly clear, of herself in her despised wedding gown, walking towards a groom whose face was an exact replica of Mike Brady's, shook her to the core.

She pulled herself up sharply. Her imagination, as well as her nervous system, seemed to be running riot. She must be in a really bad way to be responding to the obvious charms of a man such as he was: a real and practised lady-killer. Any woman foolish enough to fall in love with him would never know a moment's peace of mind.

Her telephone was ringing when she got back to her flat.

'Ms Maxwell. How would you like to have dinner with me tonight?' Mike Brady said.

Laura was almost speechless with surprise. 'Oh! I don't think——' she began, but he cut her short.

'Background knowledge is always helpful on a project. Which is why I think it might be a good idea to get to know one another on the social side.'

Laura grimaced. Hadn't last night been enough for him? It certainly had for her. Letting him get under her skin had been a mistake she wouldn't be repeating.

'How thoughtful of you, Mr Brady,' she said sweetly, 'but, with the deadline on this job, I won't have much time for socialising.'

There was a pause, and Laura could sense his irritation, but there was no trace of it in his deep, pleasant voice as he persisted. 'Don't you agree a little more insight into my character and personality would give that extra boost to your designs?'

Laura blew a silent raspberry. It would certainly give a little extra boost to your ego! she thought derisively. Strange, but he hadn't struck her as a man who would need that kind of bolstering. But then, if not that, why was he bothering? He knew Laura was soon to be married and, by his own admission, he was also about to marry. She wished she knew what game he was playing and why.

'Perhaps,' she said now. 'But, in this case, I don't think I'll have any trouble with the designs. All I need is time, and that's something I'm going to have to devote entirely to work if I'm to finish on schedule. Thanks all the same.' She made her voice extra firm, and heard him sigh.

'Do you always turn down dinner invitations as a matter of principle, Ms Maxwell, or is there something special about me?'

'Purely as a matter of principle, Mr Brady,' she answered airily. 'I assure you, you are definitely not a special case.'

The implication was deliberate, and she thought she heard him gasp. She couldn't help wondering if she'd gone too far this time. His tone of voice convinced her it was a distinct possibility.

'You never did believe in letting people down lightly, did you, Ms Maxwell?' he gritted. 'It makes me wonder why I even try——' He halted abruptly, and Laura found herself incautiously filling the gap.

'Oh, but everything's worth a try, Mr Brady.'

He gave a low, mirthless laugh, that somehow had Laura's spine tingling uncomfortably. 'Well, at least that's one thing on which we're agreed.'

'Oh, I'm sure there will be other things,' she said. Dismayingly, her tongue seemed beyond her control.

'Is that a promise?' he asked drily. 'Perhaps all is not lost after all.'

Laura squirmed. How could she have let herself in for that one? He definitely seemed to be back in control, and somewhere along the line she had a peculiar feeling that she had missed something important.

'No. Not a promise,' she answered, hanging on desperately to her cool, 'merely an observation.'

'Ah!' he said, deceptively soft. 'Well, thank you for that. But I take it dinner is still off?'

'I'm afraid so. *Bon appetit*, Mr Brady!' She put the receiver back into its rest with a peculiar sense of reprieve.

Hubert always took her out to dinner on Thursdays, but she'd felt under no obligation to explain that to Mike Brady. Let him think she had chosen deliberately to turn him down. The lesson might be salutary.

But the evening with Hubert wasn't a success. Laura made conversation that seemed, to her own sensitive ears, to be stiff and unnatural, and Hubert was quietly thoughtful. He was, apparently, just as reluctant to discuss last night's argument as she was.

In fact, he didn't speak for the whole of the journey home. As the car drew to a halt outside her flat and he helped her get out, she lifted her face for his good-night kiss, thinking it was a pleasure he might, in his present mood, decide to forgo.

But he took her by surprise. He didn't respond as usual with a light pressure of his lips against her cheek. Instead, his rather full mouth descended on her own with some force, and Laura found herself recoiling from the sensation of his moist skin against the intimate contours of her lips. It was as much as she could do to keep herself from pulling away.

Eventually, he lifted his head. His eyes seemed unnaturally bright to Laura's startled gaze, and his voice was a little ragged as he said, 'Laura, my dear. When we are married, you will choose your clients a little more selectively.'

Speechless with astonishment, she watched him walk away to his car.

Laura overslept. It was ten minutes past nine before she opened her eyes and reached groggily for the bedside clock. The shock swept away the last remnants of sleep and she shot out of bed and into the shower. Mike Brady would be here in less than an hour and she hadn't even got her brain into gear, let alone composed herself into her professional role.

Hubert was still uppermost in her mind—a strange feeling of having been allowed access to carefully hidden depths, which was alarming to say the least.

With a sigh, she stepped out of the shower and towelled herself dry.

She tried to turn her mind away from the subject, but it remained stubbornly to disturb her. The memory of the moist, probing sensation of his mouth on hers, the hard, uncomfortable pressure of his arms about her, caused a peculiar kind of churning and increased her uneasiness. Perhaps Hubert's plans for their marriage were not so undemanding as she had thought.

Their relationship was easy, if sometimes a little formal, and, to date, his kisses had been pleasant enough, stirring nothing deeper than a desire to fulfil her share of the bargain they had struck together to his apparently modest satisfaction.

That he might want, at times, to make love to her had occurred to her, of course, but the restraint of his past embraces had convinced her that it would be an inconvenience she wouldn't be asked to bear too often. It had seemed an acceptable hazard at the time. Why should it suddenly seem so distasteful?

At precisely ten o'clock, the front doorbell rang. Laura went to answer it with butterflies fluttering madly in her stomach.

The impact of Mike Brady's looks had lost none of its power, and Laura found herself fighting down a wave of excitement as she returned his easy 'good morning' with as much aplomb as she could muster and invited him into the hallway.

'You're very punctual,' she said coolly, taking her eyes from him quickly, hoping he hadn't seen in them the tell-tale flare.

'Yes!' he agreed drily. 'Punctuality is one of my little foibles.'

But not the only one, I'm sure, Laura thought grimly as she deliberately busied herself gathering her things together. She was aware that his deep blue eyes followed her every movement, but she avoided contact. She took her jacket from the stand. 'I'm ready to go to work when you are.'

His hand brushed the nape of her neck as he helped her into her jacket, and it took a tremendous effort for her to repress the shudder which began deep inside.

'Then let's go.'

She wondered if he noticed how unsteady she became on her feet as he hooked a hand beneath her elbow and led her down the front steps to his car. It was uncanny how easily her body responded to his animal charm while her brain was still capable of coolly repudiating the effect.

As she might have expected, his car was large and comfortable, gleaming silver in the cool morning sunshine, and the engine purred gently as Mike Brady pulled the car out into the press of traffic. The manoeuvre seemed to absorb all of his attention, and Laura risked a glance at him, as he sat, relaxed and coolly confident, at the wheel. The deep-set eyes, strong nose, well-shaped mouth and firm chin made a compelling profile.

The broad set of his shoulders and lean, strong hands resting lightly on the wheel did strange things to Laura's insides, and she looked hastily away. Her gaze lingered on his lips and she found herself wondering what it would be like to be kissed by him.

He turned unexpectedly and caught her look of appraisal. His smile, as Laura looked away, flustered, only enhanced the fascination of his mouth, but seemed a point against him rather than one in his favour.

'Did you enjoy Brian's party?' he asked casually, as though he hadn't felt the electric tension that crackled suddenly between them.

She might have known he wouldn't resist mentioning it. Well, he would see she could be just as cool as he. 'Yes, of course. Did you stay on long?'

He shot her a disconcerting look. 'Not too long. Marietta and I danced a little and then I took her home.'

Laura thought about him with the red-haired girl in his arms, and was jolted with shock as a forgotten memory sprang alarmingly to mind.

At some time during the long night she'd forgotten her anxieties about Hubert, and dozed off, only to be awakened by dreams of herself locked in violent, eye-scratching, hair-tearing battle with the red-headed actress, while Mike Brady looked on in amusement. Which was preposterous. She barely even knew the man, so why should her subconscious manufacture in her dreams a feeling of such fiercely possessive competition?

He wasn't looking at her now, she noted with relief. His concentration was back on the road. Just as well he couldn't get inside her head to see all the rubbish that was running riot there! She turned away, to stare pensively out of the window.

'I don't remember offering my congratulations on your forthcoming marriage,' he said, obviously continuing with his own train of thought. 'I hope you'll be happy.'

The tone of his voice seemed to imply it was a forlorn hope, and Laura bit her lip. 'Thank you,' she answered shortly, determined to steer him away from the subject. 'Do you mind if I ask you a few questions about the house?'

'Not at all.' His nod told her he understood the subject was closed. 'Just fire away.'

In between the questions and answers Laura noted that they seemed to be travelling quite a distance out into the countryside, and she wondered whether Mike Brady intended to commute each day to his office. If so, it seemed a lot of his day would be taken up in travelling.

The house came as a surprise. It was much larger than she had imagined. Almost a small manor house, in fact, standing in acres of somewhat neglected grounds. A start had already been made on renovating the outside structure, Laura noted, and there was a contractors' vehicle standing in the front courtyard.

'Good heavens!' she exclaimed as Mike Brady halted the car. 'I didn't expect anything so grand!'

'Nice, isn't it?' he affirmed casually.

'Nice is hardly the adjective,' Laura breathed. 'Overwhelming would be a better one.'

She swallowed. It was going to be a bigger job than she had imagined and, from her point of view, very much more lucrative as well, of course. But no wonder Mike Brady had been concerned about the time left to carry out the design and interior work. If he wanted it done in a hurry before the wedding, she would have to put other work in abeyance and pull out all the stops. Even then, she wouldn't have time to supervise the various stages of implementation.

'I'd better get started right away,' she said a little breathlessly. 'I'll have to stick at it really hard if I'm to get all the measurements completed today.'

'I don't expect you to kill yourself with work,' he said drily. 'Remember there's always tomorrow.'

'Not for me. I won't be available tomorrow,' she said, choosing to take him literally. 'I never work at weekends.'

She always tried, as far as possible, to give Saturday and Sunday over to Joe. They were two of the most relaxed and enjoyable days of the week, for both of them. Only if it was absolutely unavoidable would she be prepared to give one of them up.

'Ah!' He breathed the word softly and it seemed to hold a wealth of sudden understanding. 'Otherwise engaged, I take it?'

Laura knew he was thinking of Hubert. Let him think. She owed him no personal explanations.

'Something like that,' she provided brusquely. 'Now if you don't mind . . . I'd like to get started.'

'I'm sure,' he agreed with heavy cordiality. 'I'll take myself off for a word with the contractor. If you need me, just give a shout.'

'If I do, I will,' Laura assured him, sighing with relief as he left her. Without the unsettling effect of his presence, she would be much better able to keep her mind on the job in hand.

'I think it's time we had some lunch, don't you?'

Mike Brady's query startled Laura. As always, the challenge of designing had taken hold of her, and she had been too deeply engrossed in her mental images to notice he'd come into the room.

She shook her head. 'I'm not really hungry. But you go ahead. I'll be all right here until you come back.'

'You've been hard at it for over two hours. It's time you took a break.' He took the tape from her hand, set it aside, and lifted her bodily from the tall step-ladder on which she'd been standing to measure a high window. 'I'm the boss. And that's an order.'

He'd lifted her as though she weighed less than a feather, his hold surprisingly gentle for such a big man. His hands stayed on her waist as he looked down at her, and Laura felt the warm flow of his vitality running through her own body. But there was something in his eyes that had warning bells ringing loudly in her head. Her eyes were drawn unwillingly to his sensual lips, which were slightly parted as though in anticipation of a kiss.

Laura, with a sense of shock, felt the kind of sensation that one experienced at a precipice, of being drawn towards the edge, and she took an instinctive step backwards, brushing his hands from her waist.

'If you put it that way,' she said coolly, though her heart pounded with panic, 'then I suppose I have no option.'

'Quite.' He released her from his gaze, and took her elbow. 'There's an inn in the village where we can get some passable food.'

She was still trembling faintly as he handed her into the passenger-seat of the car.

He'd understated. The food at the pub was more than passable, it was delicious, and Laura found, to her astonishment, that she'd demolished every scrap put in front of her.

'I thought you weren't hungry,' he said, mildly derisive.

She flushed. 'I'd forgotten I didn't have breakfast. I'm sorry.'

'Don't apologise,' he returned politely. 'It's a pleasure to see that healthy appetite of yours at work.'

Ouch! Laura silently winced. He was obviously referring to his redhead and her pencil-slim form. Her own shapely curves must seem plump in comparison. Besides, the remark wasn't entirely underseved. This was the second time she'd made a bit of a pig of herself in his company. Was there something about him that made her subconsciously nervous?

'Point taken,' she replied, with a rueful laugh. 'Actually, this dress is beginning to feel a little tight.'

His fascinating eyes openly appraised her. 'It's filled to perfection.'

'Thanks for the compliment——' Laura flushed with irritation '—but isn't it a little over the top?'

'Not from where I'm sitting.'

Laura's flush deepened to fiery red.

'Thanks,' she said quellingly, 'but do you think we could get back to work now? The light will begin to fade soon.'

He patted her hand, which she hadn't noticed she was drumming nervously on the table.

'You seem to have a problem accepting complimentary remarks, Ms Maxwell. I should have thought a girl like you would get enough to make her blasé.'

Was that a joke? Laura tried to remember back to the last time she'd had any kind of compliment. But then, she hadn't exactly been welcoming towards the men who had shown an interest in her in the past few years.

She shrugged now. 'Compliments are superfluous to someone with a realistic appreciation of themselves.'

'True,' he affirmed gravely. 'But by whose standards do you achieve your realism?' He lifted her hand and brushed it with his lips, burning a searing path there. She was tempted to snatch it from his grasp, but knew she had to remain cool or look ridiculous. 'For instance, by my standards you're devastating.'

This time, Laura couldn't control her gasp of astonishment. He was, it seemed, deliberately assaulting her defences, which seemed annoyingly weak where he was concerned. Why, she asked herself shakily, when there was nothing to be gained? It was time to let him know she wasn't that easily taken in.

'Thanks for the ego-boost,' she said drily. 'Now I'd really like to go.'

'We'll get there, don't worry.' Mike sat back easily in his chair, his muscular legs clearly visible through the smooth, close-fitting material of his trousers. 'I think we can make time for an Irish coffee.'

Laura had begun to learn that it was useless to argue with him. As he'd said, he was the boss, and he was paying for her time. If he chose to waste some of it, then perhaps he was entitled.

In the event, she enjoyed the coffee. Whisky on its own she found unpalatable, but, disguised in the rich, dark, sweet coffee, its warmth spread quickly through her, making her feel more relaxed.

In the car, on the way back to the house, she leaned back comfortably in her seat and closed her eyes. It had been a mistake after all to have the whisky in her coffee; it made her feel deliciously drowsy.

'Tired?' His voice sounded warm...friendly. Laura opened her eyes to find his blue ones smiling into hers and, for a fleeting moment, she felt a sense of recognition, which slipped away almost before it registered.

'A little.' She gave him an answering smile. 'I had a restless night.'

He raised dark brows at her. 'How come? Excitement? Thinking about the wedding?'

She snorted a little inelegantly. 'Only to wish it was over and done with.'

He shot her a quick surprised glance. 'That's hardly a compliment to the bridegroom,' he commented laconically.

'It's not the bridegroom I object to,' she replied grimly, 'it's all the fuss of the preparations. If I'd known how the whole thing was going to snowball, I'd have——' Laura sat up and shook her head irritably to dispel the peculiar depression that was suddenly creeping over her.

What on earth had made her speak her mind in that unguarded way? The last thing in the world she wanted was to discuss her feelings about Hubert, and her forthcoming marriage, with Mike Brady. The whisky must have loosened her tongue.

'If you don't mind, I'd rather not talk about it any more.' Because if I go on even thinking about it, she added silently, I have a horrible feeling I'm going to panic.

In deference to her wishes, he left her alone to get on with the rest of the work, and she worked steadily until he came at last to interrupt her.

'How's it going?'

She gave a sigh. 'Just about finished.'

She glanced at her watch and gave a gasp. 'Oh, God! Almost five o'clock, and I'm expected at my mother's by five-thirty.'

Mike Brady frowned at her dismay. 'Is there some kind of panic on?'

She shook her head irritably. 'No. Just a promise I've made to my son Joe, and I always like to keep my promises.' Joe would be waiting for her, worrying about the light fading. 'He's at my mother's house, and I wanted to take him home to the flat this evening, but she can be very stubborn about not taking him out after dark.'

Once again, Laura was reminded that life would be very much easier for Joe once she was married.

'In that case, we'd better go.' He lifted his hand to help her down from the ladder, but she brushed it irritably aside. There was no way she was going to let him lift her down this time. 'I've always managed to run up and down ladders quite successfully without assistance, thank you.'

He sighed and stood back. 'OK, Miss Independence.'

The humorous warmth in his blue eyes was strangely unnerving. Added to the still present effects of the whisky, it made Laura unsteady. She began, with extra care, to descend, but somehow her foot caught between the two bottom steps, and suddenly she was falling, her pad and pencils flying out of her hands as she grasped at thin air to save herself.

Mike Brady caught her before she reached the ground, but not before the ankle caught in the ladder was given a painful wrench as it pulled free. She cried out and clung tightly around Mike's neck as an agonising shaft of pain shot up her leg.

'Easy!' He soothed her before sweeping her up in his arms. His voice was tight with concern. 'Take it easy.'

Feeling faint and disorientated, Laura was vaguely aware that he was carrying her out of the house. The next moment, he was lowering her gently on to the back seat of the car. He removed his jacket and rolled it up to put beneath her foot.

'That should hold it steady,' he said reassuringly. 'And fortunately there's a doctor not too far away in the village.'

'It's only a wrench,' Laura protested groggily. 'I'd much rather go home.'

'If you think you can walk home alone, then fine,' he replied grimly as he settled himself into the driving-seat. 'But I'm heading straight for the doctor.'

CHAPTER THREE

'WELL, it's not broken,' the doctor said, and Laura let out her pent-up breath on a sigh of relief. 'However, even a modest sprain can be quite painful. You'll have to stay off it for a day or so in the first instance... give the swelling a chance to go down.'

Laura sighed with relief. 'Thank goodness it isn't any worse, though even a couple of days will be a nuisance. I have to move about to earn my living. And I have so much to do before the wedding——' She broke off, filled with hopeless frustration.

The doctor's weathered face broke into a smile. 'So, you're getting married! Congratulations!'

'Thanks,' she muttered, turning pink with embarrassment as his smile scanned around to include Mike in a beam of congratulation. Perhaps she should explain, she thought exasperatedly, but for the moment explanations were beyond her.

'You're a very lucky man.' He patted Mike's shoulder paternally. 'Make sure she does as I say.'

'I'll do my best,' Mike replied, straight-faced. 'But she's not as easy to handle as she looks.'

Laura answered his mocking grin with a grimace of outrage.

'I'm sure you'll manage. A little tender loving care works wonders.' The doctor's grey eyes twinkled in Laura's direction. 'And I can see you'll have plenty of that.'

She glared stonily at Mike Brady over the doctor's head as the man bent to write out a prescription. He returned it with an amused look.

'I'm prescribing some pain-killers,' the doctor explained, handing the sheet to Mike. 'You'll find the chemist in the village open now. That foot will be throbbing and painful tonight. Make sure she has a tablet right away and another with a hot drink before she goes to sleep.'

'I'll do that, Doctor,' Mike assured him. 'Leave it to me.'

Laura flushed scarlet at the implication that Mike Brady would be around when she was ready to go to sleep, and opened her mouth to speak. Enough was enough. The doctor couldn't be allowed to go on thinking——

Unexpectedly, Mike bent and scooped her up in his arms.

'Up you come, darling,' he said outrageously. 'Tender loving care is what the doctor ordered . . . and that's exactly what you're going to get.'

Laura felt her temper rising. 'Now look here——' she began, but the doctor's benevolent smile cut her dead.

'How could you?' she raged, as soon as they were in the car and driving away from the surgery. 'I've never felt so embarrassed in my life! He obviously thought——'

'And it obviously made him happy to go on thinking it,' Mike cut in. 'So why disillusion him?'

His argument sounded almost logical, and Laura, tired and aware now of the throbbing pain the doctor had predicted, felt quite unequal to arguing the point.

'Not that it matters, I suppose,' she conceded, 'since we won't be seeing him again, thank goodness. I just wish I could lie down. Please take me straight home.' Her voice had faded almost to a whisper, and Mike shot her a concerned glance.

'We'll get the pain-killers in the village so that you can take one right away,' he said firmly, adding, with a twinkle, 'After which, we could book into the inn for the night. Purely for medicinal purposes, of course, so that I can get you to bed for a good night's sleep.'

Laura sat bolt upright with shock. 'We'll do nothing of the sort! I have to get home. Joe is waiting for me at my mother's house.'

'I'll telephone her,' he replied comfortingly, 'as soon as you're safely tucked up in bed. When I explain, she'll understand.'

'You don't know my mother. She'd annihilate a whole battalion of men to protect my reputation!' She laughed a little grimly. 'Besides, I don't think Hubert would approve of my spending the night with you. Especially not after the party——'

Laura stopped dead. Damn her careless tongue!

'The party?' he repeated. 'Ah, I see! Did you quarrel?'

'No, of course not,' Laura denied untruthfully.

He gave a short laugh. 'Strange. Had positions been reversed and I'd caught you in the arms of another man——'

'I was not in your arms,' Laura cut in hotly. 'We were dancing, nothing more.'

He shook his head. 'It felt like more to me. What a pity you weren't experiencing the same sensations.'

'Will you stop this, Mr Brady?' Laura cried fiercely. 'I'm beginning to find your warped sense of humour a little tiring.'

'I'm sorry,' he said, looking anything but apologetic. 'So the inn is out?'

'Very definitely.'

'Because Hubert wouldn't approve?'

'Precisely.' Laura eyed him coldly. 'I shouldn't think your fiancée would be any more understanding.'

His brows rose. 'I've always believed true love is based on trust. Given the circumstances, I'd expect my fiancée to understand.'

Laura searched his face for cynicism, but his expression was unreadable. 'I agree on the first part,' she told him lightly, 'but I wouldn't be too optimistic on the second.'

'Oh, but I'm always optimistic, Ms Maxwell.'

Laura bit her lip, knowing suddenly that she was out of her league. Even if she were on form, which she wasn't, with her limited experience of men she couldn't hope to beat him at a game he obviously knew so well.

'Lucky you.'

Mike smiled, but his eyes, holding hers, were cool and searching. 'I don't mind you trying to put me down. It shows you're taking an interest... and that's a start.'

A start... in what direction? Laura wondered with disquiet. Not for the first time, she wished she knew what game he was playing. He knew she was getting married, and he'd confirmed his intention to marry his glamorous redhead, so what else was left? A clandestine affair? Before either marriage had even begun? What kind of man was he?

She shuddered involuntarily. Thank goodness she wasn't 'interested'. Thank goodness, too, that she had had the strength of mind to turn down his suggestion that she stay with him at the inn. There was no telling what might have happened. For one shocking moment, her wayward mind began to imagine, before she blinked away the visions.

She shuddered again, but this time with a different effect, the tingle going right down to her toes . . . and her pulse began to race. Abruptly she gave herself a mental shake. The sooner you're married and away from shallow temptation, my girl, the better you'll be! she admonished herself.

'I'd like to go to my mother's house, if you wouldn't mind,' she said, as they turned into the little village. 'As I said, I want to get Joe—I've promised him I'll take him to the zoo tomorrow.'

He pulled the car to a halt outside the chemist's shop and turned to her with a mocking expression. 'In that case, he will definitely be out of luck tomorrow, since you're going to be somewhat restricted in what you can do for him with a painful foot.'

Laura bit her lip, inwardly acknowledging the truth of this. 'That's my problem.'

'And you're mine for the moment. Stay there while I get your tablets.'

He came back five minutes later and got back into the driving-seat. Taking a capsule from a small phial, he handed it to her with a bottle of mineral water. 'Your pain-killers! Take one now,' he said authoritatively. 'It should help, but the journey home isn't going to be easy.'

An hour later, Laura knew he'd been right. Despite the smooth running of the car, the journey back was an ordeal. Only stubborn pride kept her from crying out at anything more than the smallest movement. Her foot was swollen and puffy beneath the bandages. It throbbed uncomfortably, and it didn't help to remember that an 'ordeal by Florence' still awaited her.

Exactly as she had anticipated, when they finally arrived, her mother was on the front steps, pacing anxiously. It was dark, but the whole house and the front steps blazed with lights. Laura thought wryly that the place looked like an emergency station, and wondered what Mike Brady made of it.

Florence came down the steps towards the car.

'Laura! I've been half out of my mind with worry!' Florence greeted her. 'Where on earth have you been?'

Laura sighed. 'I've had a little accident.'

'An accident?' Florence's face paled. 'Oh, my God! Not now! So close to the wedding.'

'Thank you, Mother,' Laura returned drily. 'It's nice to see you've got your priorities in order.' She opened the car door and gingerly moved her legs over the edge of the seat. 'Fortunately, it's only a sprained ankle. I don't think I'll need crutches to get me down the aisle.'

Florence's lips set grimly. 'How on earth could you have been so careless?'

'It's only a little sprain, Mother.' Laura spoke calmly, and crossed her fingers superstitiously in her lap. 'I'll be fine by tomorrow. Where's Joe?'

Before her mother could answer, the little boy came hurtling down the steps.

'I've been waiting for you!' he remonstrated sternly, and Laura thought, disturbingly, that she could recognise her mother's influence in his indignant stance. Rescuing him from that seemed suddenly even more important. Even so, she couldn't help but smile at his lugubrious expression.

'I know, and I'm sorry.'

Joe wasn't mollified. 'You promised we'd go to the zoo tomorrow. You haven't forgotten?'

Laura bit her lip. 'No, Joe. I haven't forgotten . . . but . . .' Her voice faded tiredly.

'That's a question you'd better leave for tomorrow, Joe.' Mike Brady was there suddenly, lifting her out into his arms. 'For the moment, the only place your mother can guarantee to go is bed.'

'Put me down!' Laura protested. 'I don't have to be carried.'

'Let me be the judge of that,' he commanded.

'But I don't want to stay here for the night. I'd prefer to go back to the flat,' Laura wailed.

'On your own? With a child to look after you?' he queried impatiently. 'Don't be foolish, Laura.'

'I've sprained my foot,' she argued irritably, 'and that does not make me into a helpless invalid.'

Mike Brady ignored her, keeping her firmly in his arms, despite her struggles. He turned to Florence, who was staring aghast at the sight of her soon-to-be-married daughter being held so familiarly by a completely unknown male person. Mike smiled into her hostile face. 'I take it you do have a spare bed available for your daughter?'

'Of course.' Florence's frown deepened. 'Laura has her own room.'

He nodded his satisfaction. 'Then lead the way, if you would,' he said pleasantly. 'And I'll follow.'

Laura noted that her mother's frosty expression didn't relax, and hid a smile. If there was anyone who could put Mike Brady in his place it was Florence, and Laura had to admit there were times when her mother's sledge-hammer methods were almost welcome.

But it seemed that, for once, Florence had met her match. Mike Brady insisted on carrying her daughter up the stairs and putting her down on her bed.

'I suppose I should thank you for everything,' Laura conceded stiffly.

He shrugged. 'Don't bother if it doesn't come easy.'

Laura flushed as she acknowledged she'd been a little ungracious, which was uncharacteristic. For some reason, he seemed to bring the worst out in her, and it came as a shock to remember, suddenly, that he was a client. 'Thank you anyway. And don't worry about the work. I'll get it done, one way or another.'

'I'm not worrying. And I'll be around to make sure you do.'

Laura bit her lip in vexation. 'That won't be necessary,' she protested, but he wasn't listening.

'Put a pillow each side of that foot,' he said commandingly to Florence, who'd been hovering, obviously displeased, but strangely powerless before Mike Brady's hard stare. 'They'll help take the weight of the bedclothes off that injury.'

Laura groaned, anticipating the trouble she would have convincing her mother that Mike Brady's behaviour indicated nothing more than a civil interest.

But surprisingly, for once, Florence kept her feelings and opinions to herself, much to Laura's tired relief.

Tucked up in bed at last, she felt the comforting waves of sleep washing over her. The throbbing pain in her foot had been reduced to a dull ache by another pain-killer, and her mother had, with surprising compliance, placed a pillow each side of the injured ankle.

Laura smiled. Seeing her mother vanquished by a man's determination was a sight she had never thought to witness. She must remember to congratulate Mike Brady on his technique next time she saw him...

It must be the effect of the pain-killers, she thought woozily, but she suddenly felt very happy.

Hubert came to see her in the morning. She hadn't really expected him, since it was tacitly, and amicably, understood that her weekends were her personal times with Joe.

She guessed Florence had telephoned him, and wondered if her mother had been sensible enough to edit her version of what had happened. However, by the sternly sober expression on his face, she knew she had not. He bent to kiss her, his eyes flicking upwards to her tousled hair, with a look that was almost embarrassment.

What did he expect? Laura asked herself crossly. Did he anticipate that she would rise each morning looking impeccable? If so, then he was in for a disappointment.

Still, she had to concede that after a night such as she had just spent, kept awake by her pain and the need to keep her foot as still as possible, she probably looked more like the bride of Frankenstein than a human being.

'How are you feeling, Laura?' He sat down heavily on the little bedside chair, looking vaguely incongruous as his large bulk overflowed its edges. 'Your mother has told me what happened.' He cleared his throat delicately. 'And I'm sure there's a perfectly satisfactory explanation.'

'"Explanation"?' Her eyes opened wide. 'Do I need to explain an accident?'

He coloured faintly at her tone. 'No. Of course not. I was just worried about you.' His brows creased into a frown. 'Perhaps, on second thoughts, explanation was the wrong word.'

Laura smothered a sigh. He was even more disapprovingly pompous than usual this morning, she noted with irritation, and then immediately felt sorry. After all, having heard her mother's undoubtedly glorified version, it would be strange if he didn't express some disquiet. She wished she'd been a fly on the wall when her mother had been describing Mike Brady's part in the event.

And, of course, the fact that it had been Mike Brady and not some more innocuous client would have added to his disturbance. He was already more than a little antagonistic in that direction.

'I expect, as usual, Mother's blown the whole thing up out of all proportion,' she said, a little less sharply. 'Fortunately, I've only sprained my ankle. I'll be right as rain in a day or two, and it will be better long before the wedding; so you see you needn't have worried.'

Hubert nodded. 'Well, I'm relieved to hear that, of course.' He coughed and shifted his weight uncomfortably on the little chair.

'Um . . . Laura,' he began hesitantly, 'it was more than just . . . the accident . . . which worried me.' He looked as though he'd been asked to imbibe some particularly nasty medicine, and actually closed his eyes and swallowed before going on in a rush.

'To be perfectly frank, dear, I have given some thought to the matter, and I think it best if, in your own interests, you gave up the idea of continuing with your work after we're married, and gave your full attention to looking after the home and . . . caring for . . . your son.'

He seemed to have difficulty with the last part of his statement, Laura noted, but was almost too incensed to care about the implications. And she doubted very much if he was at all concerned about her responsibility to Joe.

'Well. That's very kind of you,' she said icily. 'But I think I am quite capable of deciding where my own best interests lie, and I most definitely will not be giving up my career. As for Joe, if you are genuinely concerned, you can rest assured he won't be neglected.'

Hubert bit his lip and reached for her hand. 'Laura, my dear, of course I'm concerned.'

'Indeed?' Laura's brows rose high on her forehead. 'Well, you have a very peculiar way of showing it. If you knew me at all well, you'd realise that I couldn't be happy without my work, and I have no intention of allowing you, or anyone else, for that matter, to dictate to me what I should do with my life.'

'But, Laura, we're going to be married. Surely you will allow me to take care of you?'

'If taking care means robbing me of all autonomy——' she shook her head vehemently '—then I certainly won't allow it.'

Hubert sat back, an expression of shocked surprise on his long, narrow face. 'My goodness! I had no idea you could be...so...' He came to an embarrassed halt.

'Determined?' Laura finished for him, pulling her hand from his. She gave a short laugh. 'Well, it's better you found out now rather than later how determined I *can* be.' She struggled into a sitting position, grimacing as she dragged her injured foot up in the bed. 'If you're looking for a submissive, obedient little wife, you'll be very disappointed I'm afraid,' she declared, her breast rising and falling agitatedly beneath the thin material of her nightgown.

Hubert's eyes seemed irresistibly drawn to her cleavage, and she noticed, for the first time, how prominent his Adam's apple was as it bobbed up and down in his throat. 'And if that's the case, perhaps we'd prefer to call off the wedding.'

His grey eyes, lifting to her face, looked pained.

'Now that's going too far, Laura! You've had a shake-up, and obviously you aren't thinking straight.' He smoothed a calming hand against her tousled hair. 'We'll discuss the matter properly when you're feeling better.'

Laura's mouth dropped open in outraged disbelief. He was simply sweeping aside what she'd said, treating her outburst as a mental aberration that was best forgotten.

'I feel better now I've seen you,' he went on comfortably. 'Unfortunately, I have to rush off right away. As I didn't anticipate this state of emergency, I'm afraid I have made prior engagements for the rest of the weekend.'

Silently, Laura gave thanks to whatever deity was overseeing her affairs. The last thing she wanted at the moment was to have Hubert fussing about her welfare.

He gave her an apologetic smile and stood up. 'But I hope to come as usual on Monday evening, if that's convenient?'

She couldn't help the sardonic laugh that bubbled up. 'I'd check in my diary, but I don't happen to have it handy.'

'I'll ignore that, Laura,' he said with a calmness that made her furious. 'By Monday you'll probably feel better.'

'I wouldn't bank on it,' she replied.

After he'd gone, she threw back the bedcovers. There was only one place she wanted to be now: her own little flat. If she kept her weight on her good foot, she could hop to the chair over which her mother had draped her clothes.

'Well! At least you're up and about.'

Laura, seated at the dressing-table to rest from the exertion of dressing, didn't need to turn around. She knew precisely who it was. Her strangely uncontrollable pulse beat out his name in rapid rhythm.

'Mike Brady! How on earth did you get in?' she exclaimed ungraciously.

'Easily.'

He touched the back of her head, and she slewed around in startled surprise. What gave him the right to think he could be so familiar?

'Then my father must have opened the door,' she guessed irritably, looking up at his tall, lean frame, immaculately clothed in casual wool shirt and trousers.

'Nope. He's in the garden with Joe. At least, I take it to be your father.'

Laura bit her lip. 'Then how...?'

He sat on the edge of the bed, studying her slim form in open appreciation, and her heart gave a leap of recognition at his strangely intimate look. 'Let me save you the hassle of surmise. Your mother opened the door to let "husband-to-be" out. Fortunately, or unfortunately, depending on your point of view, she unavoidably had to let me in.' His mouth curled cynically. 'She wanted to stay and fight it out with me, but was far too polite to let him see himself to the front gate alone. He looked more than a little surprised to see me, and it's my guess your mother will be back soon to throw me out.'

'That sixth sense of yours is right again.' Laura shifted her weight forward on the edge of the stool and put both feet firmly on the ground. 'But don't worry. I won't let her do it. From my point of view, your arrival couldn't have been more opportune. For just one more time, I need your help. I want to go home.'

'You mean back to the flat?' He seemed incredulous. 'Are you sure?'

'Very sure,' she confirmed grimly. 'That's if you don't mind driving me there?'

He shrugged. 'Well, I don't mind. But I'm sure your mother will.'

'You've guessed right again. You really have got to know my mother well on such short acquaintance, haven't you?' She gave a dry laugh. 'But I want to leave, and if there's one thing I have inherited from Florence Maxwell it's stubborn determination.'

'I have noticed,' he grinned. 'But personally I think you're being overly optimistic. In a little while you'll wish you were back in bed.'

'Give me your arm, Mike.'

His name slipped unthinkingly off Laura's tongue, and he acknowledged the familiarity with a quizzical lift of his dark eyebrows, but didn't comment.

'Not *around* me,' she said irritably as he made to lift her in his arms. 'I don't want to be carried out of here. I want to walk.'

Agonisingly hobble would better describe her progress, she thought grimly, but at least she was moving.

'Laura! What on earth are you doing?' Florence was back.

'I'm going home. Tell Joe I'm ready.'

There was no need to tell him; he was there. 'Are we going to the zoo?' His face beamed at her from the doorway.

'I don't think so,' she told him, thrusting down an unexpected feeling of helplessness. 'But we'll find a way to amuse ourselves somehow.'

'The whole idea's ridiculous!' Florence bristled with disapproval. 'Joe can stay here with his grandfather. He knows how to keep him happy. If you weren't so spoilt and selfish, Laura, you'd realise how foolish you're being.'

'If it's spoilt and selfish to want to have your own son to yourself for a couple of days, then that's what I am.' Laura set her chin firmly. 'Joe. Tell Grandpa we're going.'

'I'm here, Laura. I came to see what all the babbling was about.' Her father came into the room and stopped in astonishment as he saw her bandaged foot. 'What on earth's happened to you?'

'She took a tumble from a step-ladder,' Mike put in, ignoring a look of disapproval from Florence. 'I'm Mike Brady, and Laura was doing a job for me at the time. I brought her here last night, and now I'm prepared to take her home, if that's what she wants.'

Arthur Maxwell shook Mike's outstretched hand.

'Thank you. Unfortunately, with arthritis of my knees I find it difficult to drive these days, or I'd take her myself.'

'Don't be foolish, Arthur,' Florence protested. 'I knew if I told you what had happened you'd interfere. Laura's not going anywhere. She's staying here. Hubert wouldn't approve of her going off home with——'

'Where is Hubert?' Arthur Maxwell put in. 'If he were here, he could drive Laura himself and there'd be no need for Mr Brady to put himself to the trouble.'

'It's no trouble,' Mike assured him.

Back at the flat, Laura wasn't sure she'd made the right decision. As Mike Brady had predicted, she felt decidedly groggy and had a secret longing to go to bed and sleep, but she had Joe to consider.

From the look on his face, her son was obviously still hoping they would be able to manage his trip to the zoo. Laura ruffled his hair. 'I'm sorry, Joe. I really can't make it today.' She sat beside him at the kitchen table and turned his face up to hers. 'But I'll take you as soon as I can.' She watched ruefully as he fought his disappointment.

Mike Brady coughed and Laura started. Engrossed in the task of hobbling into the flat and soothing Joe's feelings, she'd almost forgotten him.

'Oh, I'm sorry, Mr Brady.' Laura gave him an apologetic smile. 'I'd almost forgotten you were there.'

'Thanks,' he said drily. 'There's nothing like a bit of appreciation.'

'I do appreciate your help, of course.' Laura bit her lip. 'I'm just not exactly myself at the moment.'

He shrugged. 'I know. That's why I thought you might be glad of a hand.'

She gave him a wintry smile. 'That's thoughtful of you, but quite unnecessary. I'm sure Joe and I can manage.'

He gave a short laugh. 'Now who's being unreasonably optimistic?'

She flushed. 'We'll be OK. I have a collection of board games which might be fun.'

'I'm sure.' He gave her a wry look over Joe's head. 'Can any number play?'

'Yes, of course.' She frowned. 'But I don't want to keep you. You've done enough already.'

'It was the least I could do.' He met her antagonism calmly. 'In a way I feel responsible. After all, you were injured in the course of working for me.'

Laura smiled a little stiffly. 'I don't intend to sue you, Mr Brady, if that's what you're worried about. I'm quite prepared to accept the blame for my own clumsiness.'

He laughed shortly. 'Well, that relieves my mind, though I might have been prepared to settle out of court.'

'Apart from the jokes,' Laura said coldly, 'was there anything else? I really don't feel like entertaining today.'

'That's understandable,' he replied agreeably. 'What you need is a complete rest, with that foot up. Which is why I propose taking young Joe off your hands.'

'What do you mean?' Laura stared at him, unconsciously slipping an arm about her son's shoulders. 'I don't think I understand.'

'It's really quite simple. You can rest in bed, while I take Joe out for the day.'

'I'm perfectly capable of looking after my own child,' she said sharply. 'And Joe's quite happy to wait until I can take him out myself.'

Mike Brady's eyes went to the little boy's face, and Laura followed his gaze, irritated to see that Joe's eyes had begun to glow with excitement.

'Can we go to the zoo after all?'

Mike nodded. 'If that's where you want to go.'

'Great!' Joe gave a shout of glee and was halfway out of the room before Laura could stop him. 'I'll get my jacket.'

'Now wait a minute!' Laura felt as though she were standing on shifting sands. 'I really don't think . . .'

Mike laughed. 'Give up, Laura. It's the only thing to do.' He plumped up the cushions on the settee and lifted her before she had time to protest, depositing her firmly down. 'If you won't go to bed, then rest here. And leave Joe to me. I'll take him to the zoo. I haven't been for years, and now's as good a time as any to get into practice for my intended brood.'

Laura's eyes locked angrily into his. 'You realise that you've put me into an impossible position, don't you?'

'Well, yes.' He spread his hands expressively. 'But it's for your own good.'

'My good is not your concern,' she insisted furiously. 'And I demand you leave Joe to me.'

'And disappoint him a second time?' He shook his head. 'I really couldn't do that.'

'Oh! You're impossible!' Laura growled in frustration and struggled to rise from the sofa, but he pushed her back firmly.

'I know, but there's not a lot you can do about it for now, so don't bother to argue,' he commanded. 'Where's the bedroom?'

Swamped by sudden tiredness, Laura waved a hand in the relevant direction, and he went off, coming back almost immediately with a duvet, which he placed carefully over her legs.

'I'll make you some tea before we leave.'

'But Joe doesn't know you,' Laura argued, with a return of spirit. 'You're a stranger. He'd never go with you.'

'Do you want to bet?' He grinned at Joe, who had returned and was watching, wide-eyed and solemn.

'What do you think, Joe? Is it board games at home, or the zoo?'

Laura watched Joe's usually wary look washed away by sudden excitement. 'The zoo, please!' he said jubilantly. 'And can we go right away?'

'You see? No contest,' Mike laughed, and gave Laura a surreptitious wink. 'But first things first. We'll just make sure your mother's comfortable, then we'll be off.'

Laura lay back on her cushions with a resigned sigh. There really was no point in putting up a fight any longer. She'd lost. And, for the moment, it was sweet defeat, she noted in sleepy surprise, and there was nothing she could do but enjoy the comfort and rest. The argument seemed to have sapped all her energy. Right now, it would be impossible to do anything constructive even if Mike Brady decided to take over her entire life.

What she couldn't understand was why he was doing this. What did he want? Well, whatever it was, she vowed, her anger not quite overcome by drowsiness, if he thought he could get it through Joe, he was badly mistaken.

She was asleep almost as soon as the front door closed behind them and woke in the late afternoon feeling a little brighter. She was up and hobbling about when they came back, trying to find something suitable for Joe's tea. The front door banged as she was filling the kettle.

'What are you doing up?'

Mike breezed into the kitchen, followed by a beaming Joe clutching a large stuffed giraffe. Laura wondered irritably where she would put the thing in Joe's cramped little box of a bedroom.

'I'm trying to find something to eat.' Laura's head felt like cotton wool. 'Though I'm not up to inviting you to stay for dinner.' She looked down into Joe's glowing face. 'Did you have a good time?'

'It was great. But we didn't have time to see everything. I wanted to go into the reptile house and to see the sea-lions being fed again, but Mike said we should get home just in case you weren't feeling well.'

Laura glanced at Mike. He was watching her carefully, his eyes full of something too subtle for her woolly brain to decipher. She still felt angry.

'That was kind of him,' she said, managing to inject a sharp edge of sarcasm for Mike Brady's benefit. 'But you needn't have worried. I'm fine.'

'I said you would be, and we should stay,' Joe agreed stoutly. 'But Mike said we'll go again another time to finish the tour.'

Laura groaned silently. She had a sneaking suspicion she would be listening to a lot of things Mike had said over the next few days. 'Once is enough,' she said firmly. 'Say thank you to Mr Brady for his kindness in taking you. We mustn't expect to monopolise his time.'

'I don't need an interpreter, Laura,' Mike retorted testily. 'You can speak to me directly—I do understand English.'

Laura bit her lip. It was difficult to see how she could distance herself from him enough to return to the cool, professional approach, but she would have to try.

'I'm sorry. I really would have preferred it if you hadn't done this. But, since you have, thank you.'

'And now you'd like me to go?'

'If you wouldn't mind.'

'Well, then, of course I will,' he offered amiably. 'But not before we've eaten our take-away.' He looked conspiratorially at Joe. 'I have it on the best authority that you love Chinese food. So if you'd allow us the freedom of the kitchen, we'll make you a meal fit for... what's the Chinese equivalent of a queen?'

'I don't know,' Laura said heavily, 'but——'

'Back to your couch, woman!' he commanded, and scooped her up into his arms.

'I can walk, thank you,' Laura protested, annoyed by her own awareness of the sensation of his arms about her, the hard, muscular feel of his shoulders beneath her hand as she placed it reluctantly about his neck.

'Tomorrow, you'll walk,' he said firmly. 'For now, you'll submit to being transported.'

Submit. The word echoed in her head as the clean male scent of him filled her senses. If she wasn't careful, she would find herself transported beyond the realms of common sense, she thought with a feeling akin to panic.

'Why don't you just go?' she whispered through clenched teeth.

With his lips close to her ear he whispered back, 'OK, I get the message, but don't spoil things for Joe. He's looking forward to giving you the pleasure of being waited on. It won't hurt you to pretend for a little while longer that you're enjoying yourself.'

From Joe's point of view, the meal turned into something of a party, with Mike Brady supplying the entertainment in the form of card tricks performed for the boy's obvious delight.

To Laura's amazement, Joe obeyed Mike's every word, not even protesting when he was told it was time for bed.

'I'll go if you'll read me a story,' he said, in outrageous blackmail.

'Joe!' Laura coloured in annoyance. Joe was unwittingly playing straight into Mike Brady's hands. 'Mr Brady has other things to do with his evening, I'm sure.'

Her fury mounted as he shook his head. 'You're quite wrong. I don't have anything I'd prefer to be doing right now.'

Laura fumed as Joe looked up at Mike admiringly, and then sighed with relief as she heard him say, 'Another time, Joe. Your mother's tired, and I think she's had enough of my company for the moment.'

Laura seconded that silently, and his eyes met hers in mocking understanding of her thoughts.

'Do you need a hand to wash, or anything?' he offered as Joe turned resignedly for the bathroom.

'Of course not. I can wash myself,' the boy replied with sturdy independence. 'I don't need anyone to help.'

'I can see you're your mother's son,' Mike responded drily, and Laura gritted her teeth. 'None the less, I'll see you into your pyjamas.'

She was dozing again when he came back, and woke with a guilty start. 'I'm sorry,' she said. 'I did warn you. I'm not exactly the ideal hostess at the moment.'

'It's the pain-killers. They take a while to work out of the system.' He cleared a space for himself at the foot of the sofa and took her hand in his. 'And don't worry about me, I'm having a wonderful time.'

'I'm glad one of us is,' she responded sourly, removing her hand from his.

He laughed and brushed the damp tendrils of hair from her temple. Laura gasped with shock at the electric contact of his touch and the strange expression in his deep blue eyes. He leaned forward as though he was about to kiss her, and she pulled back sharply.

'I hope you don't mind seeing yourself out?' she asked pointedly.

'Not at all,' he said, maddeningly courteous. 'You rest that foot, and don't worry about a thing.' He touched her hair again in that gesture of familiarity that had her seething. 'And remember, if you need any further help, just give me a call.'

CHAPTER FOUR

LAURA was surprised to find she'd survived the night without being wakened by discomfort from her foot, and this morning it was sore and stiff but without the nagging ache of yesterday. It was possible to walk provided progress was slow and careful.

She'd been slow getting off to sleep, haunted by the expression she had last seen on Mike Brady's face and by the promise in his parting words. He was too powerful, she admitted with a groan, wishing she'd been strong enough to tell him last night to keep away. She'd slept eventually, but woke with a feeling of restlessness, which quickly transferred itself to Joe.

'I want to go out to the park,' he pronounced with uncharacteristic firmness, as soon as he'd finished his breakfast.

Normally, he sat quietly playing or painting while she tidied away the breakfast things and then dealt with the morning's chores, but today he wore a fretful look of impatience. Laura wondered if it mirrored her own expression. He certainly looked the way she felt.

Mike Brady's whirlwind take-over of yesterday had left eddies of disturbance which refused to settle. She'd half expected him to capitalise on his advantage last night, but he hadn't, being wise enough, Laura thought sourly, not to push too far too soon. But he'd moved far enough.

Joe was probably missing his hero this morning, she thought, with a feeling of disquiet. She should not have allowed yesterday to happen, but there hadn't been much she could do about it.

'OK, bossy boots,' she ruffled his thick hair. 'The park it is, and hang the dishes! But, since I'm still a bit of an invalid, we'll have to take it slowly.'

The sun was shining after a night of heavy rain, and the world seemed washed and gleaming and ready for a new start, and Laura, hobbling along with Joe, felt peculiarly like a lame horse at the gate straining to join the race but knowing she'd never make it.

She shrugged the nonsense away. She knew where she was going. She'd been travelling the road for years and now was in walking distance of her destination. Freedom, independence, but with the security of a firm base. All of which would be achieved by her marriage to Hubert. Why, then, did she shudder? And why should her mind's eye be full of Mike Brady?

She frowned, creasing the smooth skin of her forehead. All day yesterday she had been aware of the pressure to which he had been subtly subjecting her. If he, or anyone else, for that matter, were to ask her to define the pressure, she would have trouble doing so, except to say that somehow she felt threatened by him, and was aware of a strong need to be wary. But was it of him? Or her own strangely volatile emotions?

She sat on a bench as Joe, having found a friend, ran off to play on the swings. She could keep an eye on him from where she sat.

'Good morning.'

Laura's head slewed around in surprise at the sound of the deep, familiar voice.

Mike Brady sat down beside her. 'I had trouble parking the car, or I'd have found you earlier.'

Laura felt the knot of anger form in her stomach. 'How did you know where to find me?'

He looked quite devastating this morning, she noted, casually dressed in an open-necked short-sleeved shirt and trousers, and with his hair ruffled by the faint breeze. His forearms were lightly tanned and muscular, with a fine covering of brown hair.

'I was just arriving as you left the house. I sounded the horn, but you were too engrossed with the little fellow to notice.'

'Oh!' Laura said inadequately. 'But then, I wasn't expecting to see you again so soon.'

He studied her face, which was faintly pink with annoyance. 'You don't sound too pleased that you have.'

'As a matter of fact I'm not,' she told him directly. 'Whatever responsibility you might have felt for my accident, you discharged it yesterday. Now, I really would prefer to keep our relationship on a more formal basis.'

He nodded slowly. 'I see.'

'I'd be relieved if you did.'

He frowned. 'Meaning?'

'Meaning,' she responded in annoyance, 'that you don't seem the type of person to mix business with pleasure, and I can't help wondering why you choose to do so in my case.'

'It couldn't be plain old-fashioned concern?' His brows rose mockingly.

'Possible, I suppose,' Laura conceded grudgingly. 'But unlikely—and there's no need. I'm definitely on the mend.'

He nodded. 'I'm relieved to hear that.'

'And there's Gladstone House, of course,' she went on edgily. 'If you're worrying about the job, then don't. Work will go ahead, just the same.'

'That's good news too,' he acknowledged with a smile that put that fascinating fold into his cheek, and Laura had to tear her eyes away from the distraction.

'Apart from all that, how's the foot this morning?'

'Difficult,' she said coolly, 'but getting better.'

'I don't think walking in the park was quite the right choice.'

'Perhaps not. But with an active four-year-old on my hands I don't have too many choices that don't entail mobility.'

'Exactly. Which is why I thought you might appreciate a trip around Designers' Choice on a quiet Sunday. Today you'd have the place to yourself and you could move at your own pace. I could even dig up a wheelchair from the works surgery if you got tired. It would be no trouble to push you around.'

She stared at him. When would the man get the message?

'I already have a very good idea of most of the Designers' Choice ranges on which to base my initial designs. I'll be almost finished before I need to pay an actual visit to the store.'

His eyes narrowed mockingly. 'And you haven't the smallest curiosity about our latest lines? Wouldn't you like to see the way the fabrics are printed and finished?'

She gave a short, impatient laugh. 'I did all that when I was at college. Your company used to send lecturers there to talk about your products, and arrange guided tours for those who were interested. Don't you remember, or perhaps that was before your time?'

'No, it wasn't, and of course I remember. I initiated the arrangement myself.' His mouth curled faintly. 'Perhaps it's you who should consult your memory.'

Laura was suddenly staring at him as a door in her mind creaked open. 'We have met before, haven't we? But you wouldn't admit it!'

He nodded slowly. 'I was waiting to see how long it took you to remember...to see how much of an impression I'd made.' He grimaced. 'Not very much, I'd say, judging by your tardy response.'

Laura frowned. 'You lectured when I was there, didn't you?' Her frown deepened as the memory expanded. 'And afterwards...you asked me out to dinner!' Her mouth opened in astonishment. How could she have forgotten that so completely? she asked herself incredulously. Those amazing good looks of his should have been burned indelibly on to her inner vision. He was definitely a man who, once seen, was never forgotten.

'That's right. And you turned me down.' He gave a short, hard laugh. 'Not very kindly, as I remember.'

'Did you expect kindness?' she queried a little sarcastically. 'As *I* remember it, you were more than a little persistent.'

'I always am——' his eyes narrowed on her '—when I'm after something I particularly want.'

Laura stared back at him, her curiosity aroused at last. 'It hurt, did it, Mr Brady?' she said, softly jeering. 'Having a woman turn you down, I mean. I don't suppose it happens very often.'

'Fortunately not.' His mouth twisted ironically. 'Did you enjoy being the exception?'

'I really have no recollection,' she said haughtily. 'I expect I did. I imagine I would have found you overbearingly conceited and in need of a put-down.'

He snorted sharply. 'Oh, you did that all right. I wondered for a long time afterwards why such a beautiful woman found it necessary to be so cruel.'

The memories came stinging back. No wonder she hadn't wanted to remember. Mike Brady was tied up with the most painful time of her life. A time when she'd found out that the man she'd married hadn't really loved her. He'd died before she found that out.

There had been three damp-eyed and lovely women at his funeral—his spare-time co-stars—and Laura realised then that it had been more than just his work which had kept him away from home.

'I was once married to a very handsome man, Mr Brady,' she revealed tightly. 'Like you, he didn't consider a commitment to one woman any reason not to pursue others.'

The line of his mouth thinned. 'Still as forthright as ever, Ms Maxwell,' he observed chillingly. 'Do you intend to go on forever tarring any man who isn't downright ugly with that same brush?'

'I doubt whether I'll be giving men much thought, one way or the other, from now on. Once I'm married——'

Mike moved suddenly to grasp her shoulders and turn her to face him. 'So you think you'll be safe...married to that dead-pan Hubert Laine?' he said vehemently. 'Well, I wouldn't count on it. Men are men despite the accident of their looks. And if that's the reason you're marrying him, then someone ought to wake you up to the truth before it's too late.'

'That person being you, I suppose,' she bit back furiously. 'Thanks. But I really don't think you're that altruistic. You just can't believe that I could prefer someone like Hubert to you.' She tossed her head challengingly. 'Well, let me tell you, Mr Wonderful Brady, that it takes more than good looks and charm to——'

He grinned suddenly, but there was no humour in his eyes. 'So you have noticed?' he cut in.

'I've noticed,' she bit back. 'I'd have to be blind not to know your looks are out of the ordinary. Unfortunately, as far as I'm concerned, they're more of a minus than a plus.'

'Is that so?'

He grabbed her suddenly into his arms, his mouth crushing down on hers so forcefully that it took her breath away. Fury mingled with unwilling excitement as the kiss went on. Laura's head buzzed with the sensations his lips were arousing and, even as some tiny part of her mind rebelled against being forcibly made love to in public, some other part of her wanted it to go on, to give her time to explore the reasons why this felt so different.

She gasped with shock as he suddenly lifted his mouth from hers and pushed her away. He looked angry, as though it were she who had been forcing him into the embrace.

'Was that meant to prove something?' she demanded furiously.

He gave a cynical laugh, his deep blue eyes searching hers mercilessly. 'Are you telling me it didn't?'

Laura's breath hissed in through her clenched teeth. 'I don't have to tell you anything,' she gritted, adding on a burst of temper as he continued to gaze at her challengingly, 'Oh, why don't you just go away and leave me alone?'

'All right.' He stood up and looked down at her mockingly. His eyes went to her bosom, which was still rising and falling on jagged breaths of fury and excitement. 'If you're sure that's what you want.'

Laura's mouth tightened into a thin line. 'Just go!'

He nodded. 'OK. Maybe I'll give you a ring in the week . . . to see how you're getting on . . .' He held up his hands as her mouth opened angrily. 'I mean, with the plans for Gladstone House, of course.'

'That won't be necessary . . .' she began, but he was already walking away. He waved across to Joe, but he was gone before the little boy came running across.

Joe reached her knee breathless and looked up at her in obvious disappointment. 'Where's Mike gone? Isn't he taking us out today?'

'No. He came to see me on business.' She smoothed his head. 'He's a client, Joe. Not a friend. He won't be taking you out again.' Laura could have wept to see Joe's crestfallen expression, and she heaved a deep, shuddering sigh.

After today, she decided firmly, she would keep herself—and Joe—well out of Mike Brady's way. It would be better all round . . . for everybody's peace of mind.

Mike Brady telephoned a few days later to enquire after her progress and to ask if she would like to have dinner with him. She'd intended simply to be evasive but, when he asked after Joe, she decided the direct approach would be the best.

'He's fine. But I don't think you ought to see him again.'

There was a pause before he answered carefully, 'He didn't like me?'

Laura made a soft, impatient sound. 'You know better than that. He liked you too much, and that's the trouble. He's very young and impressionable and . . . for the moment . . . a little short of male company. But that will be remedied soon.'

'I see . . .' Mike said slowly.

'I hope you do,' Laura rushed on before her resolution failed. 'Because I don't want him thinking of you as a permanent fixture in his life.'

'Ah, that's it!' he said slowly. 'Or in your life either, I presume?'

Laura swallowed, trying to clear the constriction in her throat. 'I'm getting married, Mike,' she reminded him rather shakily. 'And so are you.'

Softly, he queried, 'And does that mean we can't be friends?'

'It means . . .' Laura hesitated '. . . that I'd prefer it if we weren't.'

He gave a short, bitter laugh. 'I see.' He sighed, before adding so softly she almost didn't hear it, 'I thought, this time, we might have made it.'

CHAPTER FIVE

IT WAS halfway through a wakeful night that the penny suddenly dropped. Laura hadn't remembered Mike Brady, but he had most certainly remembered her. How could he fail to recognise the woman who had rejected him so bitterly? She guessed cynically that no woman had done it before, nor probably since. A painful experience for a man like Mike Brady, used to getting what he wanted just because he wanted it, and one he'd be unlikely to forget in a hurry.

What must he have felt when he'd come unexpectedly face to face with her again? He couldn't have failed to notice that his looks had bowled her over. Had he thought then that revenge would be sweet? Was that what this was all about now?

Suddenly, his last remark made sense. This time, he'd thought he'd won!

Laura twisted and turned in her bed. She had almost begun to fall for it...to believe in his friendship. How could she have been so stupid...let her guard down so easily, after the way she'd been hurt in the past?

But the most hurtful thing of all was the way he had ingratiated himself with Joe...just to get back at Laura. If she had any pride—any common sense—she would take care to protect herself, and Joe, from any further harm from him. In future, contact with Mike Brady would be kept to a minimum, she vowed.

Very soon, she would finish the job he'd given her, and there would be no further excuse for him to see her. She would marry Hubert and take up the disturbed threads of her life, making them strong again.

He didn't try to contact her again, which she told herself was a relief. Immersing herself in the Gladstone House designs, she worked doggedly—creating, rejecting, polishing, winding steadily towards the finished design.

Then it was time, she realised, with a sinking sensation in the pit of her stomach, that she made her visit to Designers' Choice. It was silly to let it matter, she knew, but she didn't want Mike Brady to be there.

She chose her time carefully, as near to lunchtime as possible, reasoning that he would probably take extended lunch-hours. But, as it happened, he was there when she turned into the street leading to the front entrance. He was standing in front of the window, with Marietta hanging on his arm.

Ducking into a convenient doorway, Laura watched them. Marietta's free hand was waving expansively at various items of furniture in the window. Mike had an indulgent look on his face, and nodded his approval from time to time.

What on earth was happening? Was he allowing Marietta to choose items for Gladstone House? As his prospective bride, of course, she would normally have every right. But Mike was paying Laura to create a co-ordinated design. He'd informed her of his own preferences in the beginning, which she'd incorporated, but he hadn't asked for Marietta's views to be taken into consideration, and it was too late now. Laura bit her lip hard to stem the rise of temper. Was he really that thoughtless, or was it an indication of how little the actual designs for Gladstone really mattered to him? Had the whole project merely been a lever... an apparently legitimate means of gaining entry into her life to enable him to wreak his revenge?

They were moving away from the window, coming her way, and Laura pressed herself further back into the doorway, dreading the thought that they might see her. But as they drew near she was filled with an almost overwhelming urge to rush out and challenge him, then and there, on the spot. It would give her great satisfaction, but she knew it would be a mistake.

In her present state of angry confusion, it was hard to decide which feelings were uppermost—anger at Mike Brady for the deep pain of his betrayal or her hatred for Marietta.

She made her way through the relevant departments of Designers' Choice almost on automatic pilot. Mike Brady had been right; there were many new lines which would have held her fascinated in different circumstances, but her heart wasn't really in the business of choosing.

She woke the next morning weighed down by a strange and uncomfortable lethargy. Her breakfast coffee was extra strong, but did little to revive her spirits.

She heard the rattle of the letter-box and the thud of mail hitting the carpet, and went, heavy-eyed and listless, to retrieve it. The doorbell shrilled as she stood in the hallway sifting through the envelopes. The postman, she surmised, with a parcel which was too large for the letter-box. Probably the samples she'd ordered from Mike Brady's store.

And why hadn't he mentioned he owned Designers' Choice when he had first stipulated their ranges? She had thought he was extravagant, but realised now that fitting out his house in the height of good taste and luxury would cost him nothing. Somehow, it added to her uncharacteristic peevishness.

The bell pealed again, and she looked hastily into the mirror. Her face was pale and drawn, evidence of her disturbed night, and her hair had yet to feel the restraining influence of a brush. She ran her fingers through it hastily, and opened the front door. Her hand was already raised in a gesture of acceptance, and remained frozen as she stared into the handsome face of Mike Brady.

Gravely, he placed a parcel into her grasp. 'The samples you requested,' he said with a twinkle in his blue eyes. 'I thought I'd deliver them personally.'

Laura, aware of a peculiar melting sensation, stiffened her resistance and refused to smile back at him. 'There wasn't any need for that,' she said stiffly, watching with sour satisfaction as the teasing light disappeared. 'But thank you all the same.'

He frowned a little. 'My gesture doesn't warrant a cup of coffee?'

Laura bit her lip. 'I'm not dressed for visitors,' she said doggedly. 'And, besides, I'm too busy for socialising.'

His frown deepened. 'This isn't entirely a social call. I was hoping to have a glimpse of the designs.'

He moved nearer, and Laura felt the now familiar tremor. It added to her anger, knowing this assault of her senses was deliberate, planned...a means to an end. After all, her ideas for the house could hardly be that important if he was actively encouraging Marietta to make choices without even seeing the finished designs. But then, as long as he paid her for her work, she argued silently, why should she care what mess he and Marietta made of the house?

'I'd rather you didn't. At the moment, they're fairly basic ideas. I'll be making considerable changes before they're anywhere near complete enough for you to see, which won't be for a fortnight or so.'

'Ah, I see!' He sighed. 'Disappointing. But I don't wish to rush you.'

'Thank you.' Laura put her hand on the door in a gesture of dismissal. 'Then you don't mind if I get on?'

He shook his head vexedly. 'Look here, Laura! Have I done something to offend you?' He moved forward to block the doorway, and put a gentle hand on her shoulder, sending instant heat through her body. 'If I did, you must know I didn't mean to.'

Laura gave a cynical inwards laugh, but aloud she said, 'Why should you think you've offended me?'

He made an impatient sound. 'Well, you're hardly welcoming, are you? And I shouldn't imagine you mete out this kind of treatment to all your clients. Or do you?'

'No, of course I don't!' she cried, shrugging off his hand. 'But not every client tries to mix business with pleasure the way you do.'

He paused, his eyes scrutinising her tense, furious face.

'Is that what I've been doing?' An ironic smile curved the corners of his mouth. 'Well, I don't recall that much pleasure.' He pulled her suddenly into his arms, lifted her off her feet and, with a backward kick, shut the front door behind him.

Before Laura had time to protest, his mouth descended fiercely on hers, moving against her sensitised lips with devastating effect, shocking her into response. With her head spinning, she felt herself being drawn into a whirlpool of sensations she'd never known existed . . . whorls of heat and cold . . . surprise and delight . . . devastation . . . His hands, moving against her back, the curve of her waist, brought an excruciating pleasure that had her almost crying out.

It took every ounce of strength she could muster to stiffen her melting body in his arms, to keep hands that longed to cling to him clenched tightly against his chest, resisting his attempts to mould her against him.

As her resistance hardened, he relaxed his hold and put her away from him.

'You almost came alive then, Laura.' With his hands on her shoulders, he shook her none too gently. 'That is, before you took your bloody shovel and buried yourself again in the past.'

Laura's breath was short and ragged with shock. With just one kiss he seemed to have penetrated to the very core of her being. But it went further than that, she knew.

'I suppose you know what you're talking about?' she challenged shakily.

'I do.' He nodded, his eyes looking deep into hers, searching out the shadows lurking in the corners. 'And so do you.'

Laura gasped at the certainty of his tone. What had he seen? What was still there to see? All the furtive hopes and yearnings she had smothered to extinction years ago? All the solidly built and nurtured defences she'd erected around herself revealed suddenly, before his gaze, as transparent as the thinnest tissue paper?

His hand cupped her cheek tenderly.

'There's more to life than security, Laura. Sometimes it's only the risks we take that make life worth living.'

'"Risks"?' she echoed bitterly. 'Oh, yes! I know all about risks. I was married to a man who lived for nothing else. Not his wife...not his child——' She caught herself up sharply. She'd actually been on the point of revealing herself completely to him. To a man who was bent only on his own shallow revenge.

'Oh, no! I leave risks to people like you, Mr Brady, who haven't yet learned how...fatal...they can be.' She smiled thinly. 'Nowadays, I play for safety.'

He nodded calmly. 'Is that why you're marrying a man you don't love?'

Laura took a sharp breath. 'I don't remember saying I don't love Hubert.' Colour rose furiously to her cheeks and she tried desperately to remember just what she had said to him that day, under the influence of whisky.

'There are some things that don't have to be said,' Mike insisted reasonably. 'But I agree appearances can be deceptive.'

He moved a lock of hair which had fallen across her cheek and tucked it behind her ear, his fingers lingering there exploringly with electric results. 'Are you telling me now that you do love him?'

Laura shrugged away from his touch. 'My reasons for marrying are my business. And I'd be glad now if you would leave.'

She drew herself up to her full height, though she barely reached to his shoulder.

'Or else...?' His smile was laconic. 'I take it you'll personally throw me out?'

Laura glared determinedly at him. 'I might.'

'In that case, I suppose I'd better retire gracefully.'

She nodded, holding on precariously to her temper and her poise. 'That would be nice.'

He turned and opened the front door, pausing there to look back at her. 'I assume I'll be hearing from you when the designs are ready for me to take a look?'

She nodded. 'Of course. But, as I explained, that won't be for a while.'

He gave a resigned sigh and said softly, 'Give Joe my best regards.'

Laura's face was wooden. 'He doesn't need them, Mr Brady. And in future I'd be glad if you'd keep away from him. He's been hurt enough already.' Before he had time to answer, she pushed him out of the door and slammed it behind him. Then, for long seconds, she stood with her back to the door, breathing quickly and full of a painful kind of confusion. Had she been talking about Joe... or herself?

For a while, Laura half expected to hear from him, or perhaps his secretary, to the effect that he no longer required her services, but after nearly a week had passed she felt able to push on with the rest of the designs more confidently. Whatever he might think of her behaviour, he obviously still wanted her to complete the job.

She worked late and got up early the following morning, determined to finish the whole project now as quickly as possible.

Deeply engrossed in her design for the nursery, Laura found the high-pitched sound of the telephone a nerve-shredding intrusion.

'Laura!' Florence's commanding tones rang down the line. 'You must come over to tea this evening. The designs for the cake have arrived and I want you to help me choose.'

Laura gritted her teeth. 'I'm busy, Mother. Can't you do it yourself?'

'Well, really, Laura!' Florence was astounded. 'Don't you have any interest in your own wedding at all? Any *normal* bride would be thrilled.'

Laura groaned. But then, I'm not a normal bride, am I? she said to herself. In fact, I'm practically dispensable.

Up until today, Florence had appeared to have abandoned all idea of involving Laura in the wedding arrangements and, absorbed in the Gladstone House designs, Laura had almost forgotten the big event. Still, she supposed it was unrealistic to expect that she would be allowed to escape completely scot-free.

'All right,' she capitulated grudgingly. 'I'll come to tea.'

Her mother was almost cheerful these days, busy with the schedule of events and all the practicalities of co-ordinating the perfect wedding, and Laura was more than happy to let her get on with it.

Her father seemed happier, too, Laura noted. He had Joe almost completely to himself, with little interference from Florence, and on the one or two occasions they'd clashed over the little boy's welfare Laura had been amazed to see him holding his corner against her mother. She couldn't help suspecting that, after the dust of the wedding had died down, her father might be planning one or two surprises of his own for Florence.

He was in the garden, standing in goal for her footballer son. When he saw Laura, he waved to Joe to tell him he was taking a rest and went and sat on the bench.

'How's Hubert?' he asked.

Laura hid her surprise at the unusual query.

'Fine, as far as I know. I haven't seen him for a while. He's busy.'

'Hm. Yes.' Arthur Maxwell frowned. 'You're marrying what seems to be a very busy man. Are you sure you want to?'

Laura's spine tingled unpleasantly. How could she have forgotten that that absent air of her father's hid a very astute intelligence? 'Nothing wrong with that where I'm concerned,' she said defensively. 'I'm busy myself. And why shouldn't I be sure?'

'You tell me.'

Laura sat down beside him, not wanting to face him directly in line with his deceptively mild eyes.

'Have you been seeing any more of that young chap who was here the night of your accident? Mike Brady? Joe seems to have taken quite a fancy to him.'

Laura shifted uncomfortably. So Joe had mentioned his weekend outings with Mike Brady after all. She supposed she should be grateful he had chosen her father to confide in instead of her mother.

'Yes. I know,' she said lightly. 'But he's just a client, Dad. And Joe won't be seeing any more of him. Neither will I, after the wedding.'

'Hmm.' Her father sucked on his cold pipe. 'Pity. I took quite a fancy to him myself.'

Laura tutted impatiently. 'Don't be silly, Dad. You hardly know him.'

He gave her a sharp look. 'There are times, Laura, when you sound almost like your mother.'

'That's the worst thing you've ever said to me,' Laura joked, but her laugh sounded uncertain. 'I hope you're teasing.' She stood up. 'Speaking of Mother, I suppose I should go in and announce my arrival.'

He caught her arm. 'Hold on!' He took Laura's hand in his, and she saw, with astonishment, that his eyes were moist. 'Don't settle for less than you deserve, Laura. If you did, I don't think I could bear it.'

Laura wished her father hadn't chosen to voice his worries just now. The tension of the wedding seemed to be getting to them all. From her point of view, the deadline on Gladstone House had turned out to be a blessing. It stopped her from winding herself up.

Just as fortunate was Hubert's own preoccupation with business. It had saved her the worry of having to maintain their usual routine. Consequently, when he turned up on Monday evening she'd completely forgotten that he was coming to take her out to dinner.

It was an added annoyance to find, when they arrived at the restaurant he'd chosen, that Brian Huxley was there with Marietta Strang. There was a third chair at their table, and Laura thought, with a groan, that they were probably waiting for Mike Brady to join them. She would have liked to turn tail and run, but couldn't face finding an explanation for Hubert.

When the head waiter came to guide them to their table, Laura pointed to an empty one at the far side of the room, and sighed with relief when the man nodded.

'You wish to sit there? Certainly, madam.'

Despite a resolve to ignore their presence, Laura found her eyes straying to Brian and Marietta, who had, fortunately, been too engrossed to notice her entrance. Marietta looked happy—and why shouldn't she? Laura thought with sudden bitterness. Soon she would be married to Mike Brady and living in his lovely house...reaping the benefits of all Laura's frenzied hard work.

And she's welcome to both! Laura declared silently. I just hope she knows what she's letting herself in for. With a man like Mike Brady, nothing could ever be taken for granted, but Marietta undoubtedly thought the rewards merited the risks.

With sudden, searing clarity, Laura remembered how it had felt to be held in his arms, the burning thrill of his mouth against hers, her own weak longing to surrender.

Why couldn't it have been real, she thought hopelessly, instead of just his way of making even an old score? It all seemed suddenly very unfair. What on earth is the matter with you? she admonished herself disgustedly. Fairness doesn't come into anything. You're being paid to do a job, and once it's over... But her mind refused to go beyond that inexplicably painful point.

On a kind of automatic pilot, she ate and drank and responded to Hubert's attempts at conversation. Fortunately, he too seemed preoccupied, and content, for the most part, to eat his food in silence, a tiny frown between his pale brows.

Mike Brady didn't turn up.

Tense and confused, Laura couldn't decide whether it was a relief or a disappointment. She stole a look at Marietta's pretty face, wondering how she was feeling about Mike's non-appearance. She was smiling at Brian, flirting with him outrageously, undoubtedly to cover up her rage. It was a brilliant performance, Laura conceded grudgingly. The girl probably had a wonderful future as an actress ahead of her . . . if she could find a way to fit it in between Mike's anticipated babies . . .

Back at her flat, Hubert insisted on coming in.

Laura acceded with a heavy heart, wondering at this unusual change in his routine. She made him coffee in the small kitchen, and carried it through to the living-room, where he sat on the sofa, his chin sunk on his chest, his eyes apparently focused on his own inner thoughts.

Laura had a sudden ominous premonition. Hubert had something on his mind, and she wasn't going to like hearing about it. He put his cup down on the side-table without even tasting his coffee.

'I'm sorry if I appear to have been neglecting you lately, Laura,' he began. 'But it's been as much for your sake as for mine.'

'I haven't minded, Hubert. Really I haven't.'

'But you should mind,' he insisted. 'A beautiful woman like you shouldn't be neglected.' He turned to her and grasped her hands, and Laura noted, with disquiet, that his grey eyes were over-bright with a kind of fervour. 'But things will be different. I promise. Once we're married, I'm going to devote myself entirely to you.'

Silently, Laura groaned. The last thing in the world she wanted now was Hubert's devotion.

'It isn't necessary, Hubert,' she argued a little desperately. 'I don't feel neglected . . . or ignored. And I need time for my own work, just as you do.'

He grasped her shoulders. 'All that is unimportant. What matters is that we should be together. Learning to know each other more . . .' he hesitated before going on '. . . more . . . intimately, perhaps, than we have in the past.'

She found herself shuddering at his implication of greater intimacy, but it was a bridge she knew she would have to cross when she got there.

His arms came around her suddenly, holding her against him. Unexpectedly, his mouth came down on hers, and Laura recoiled from the probing of his hot, moist tongue. His hold on her tightened, until he seemed to be crushing the breath from her body.

Laura gave a little cry and began to struggle, pushing against his chest until his head lifted. 'Hubert. For heaven's sake!'

He let go of her with a start, and moved back. 'I . . . I'm sorry,' he stammered. His face was fiery red and he was panting. 'I'm . . . afraid . . . I . . . let my feelings . . . run away with me.'

She stared at him, at a loss for words, shocked by the feeling of revulsion that was shuddering through her body. This was the man she was going to marry soon. Yet she felt soiled by his kiss.

Almost immediately, she began to rationalise. It was because she'd been unprepared, she told herself. It was so totally unlike Hubert that she hadn't expected to arouse such a strong show of feeling in him.

'That was unforgivable of me, Laura, I know.' Hubert's face was a deep shade of red as he struggled to regain his dignified composure. 'I should have shown more respect. A woman like you deserves that...' His voice trailed off.

Laura felt a wave of compassion sweep over her. She couldn't, in all honesty, blame him...go on listening to him apologising for being a man...when it was her lack of response that had made the whole thing seem wrong.

It was up to her to sort out her priorities. 'Forget it, Hubert,' she said gently. 'I have.'

It wasn't strictly true, but she vowed determinedly that she would do her best to make it so.

Laura was shaking from head to foot as she closed the front door behind him. Slowly, she went into the living-room and sank down on to the sofa, trying to find some order amid the confusion of her mind.

The wedding loomed suddenly, a spectre so huge and overpowering that she was tempted to ring her mother and tell her she couldn't go through with it.

Florence would probably die of shock.

Life for her mother had been a series of cruel disappointments. How could she heap another upon Florence's martyred head? It was unthinkable.

Somehow, Laura vowed, she would have to come to terms with the fact that she had made her bed, and find some way of ensuring she could lie in it.

But, for now, there was the solace of work.

CHAPTER SIX

'DAMN . . . and damn again!' Laura swore softly to herself. 'How could I have been so stupid?'

She checked once more through her notes, but there was no mistaking the fact that she had taken two separate and quite different sets of measurements for the same window alcove.

She stood up and paced the floor restlessly. Now she would need to ask Mike Brady for the keys to the house in order to re-measure. The last thing in the world she wanted was to have to make contact with him again, especially after she'd virtually thrown him out of the flat. It was possible he might think she was just looking for an excuse to see him again.

After a short battle with her pride, Laura rang him. This was, after all, business, and from now on she would make sure it remained strictly that way.

His voice was unexpectedly friendly. 'Laura! How nice!'

Her treacherous pulses began to race. 'Mike! I'm afraid I've made an error in one of the measurements.' She kept her voice level. 'Do you think I could have the keys to the house to re-measure?'

'No problem.' His voice was as even as hers. 'In fact, I could drive you out there this morning if you like——'

'That won't be necessary,' Laura broke in hastily. 'I know the way, and I won't be staying long.'

She heard him sigh.

'OK. Do you want me to drop the keys over on my way to the office, or would you like to call here at the flat?'

'I'll call,' Laura said quickly. 'If you'll just give me the address?'

'Fine.' He dictated his address.

'Don't bother to wait,' Laura told him. 'Just leave an envelope with the caretaker.'

'OK. If that's how you want it.' He sounded cheerfully offhand.

Laura felt inexplicably rebuffed. Had she expected him to argue? Had she wanted him to?

The house was different without Mike Brady in it. Unaccountably it seemed to have lost its vivacity and become just an empty house awaiting its new occupant.

The wrongly measured window alcove was in the larger drawing-room. It was tall and elegant, and its height would require the use of the long step-ladder, which, annoyingly, was no longer in the room.

She searched all over the house, before coming to the conclusion that someone must have stored it away somewhere. A further search of likely cupboards and recesses was equally fruitless, and eventually she went outside into the garden in search of anything which would assist.

It had begun to rain and there were dark clouds gathering on the horizon, driven by a fresh wind that tugged at her skirt as she looked around for a likely storage place. There were a number of outbuildings close by, and it was through the window of one of these that she eventually espied the step-ladder.

She gave a grunt of satisfaction, which turned quickly to consternation. The door was heavily padlocked. Laura relieved her feelings of frustration with a sharp kick to the stout wood, and gave a loud curse as a shaft of agony shot up her leg.

'Unladylike. But very understandable.'

A deep, amused voice sounded close behind her. She knew who it was even before she spun around, and so had time to compose her expression, which was a mixture of dismay and reluctant joy.

'Mike,' she said sharply, meeting his sardonic gaze, 'I told you I could manage alone.'

He laughed again. 'And then found you couldn't.'

Colour stung her cheeks. 'It's not my fault the stepladder had been tidied away.'

'Agreed,' he nodded reasonably. 'Which is why I've brought the key to the outhouse.'

He opened the door and took out the ladder.

'I realised you might need it almost as soon as I'd left the flat, but the traffic held me up on my way back, and when I got there you'd already been and gone.'

Despite herself, Laura was glad he'd come, and she made no protest as he insisted on holding the ladder for her.

But it was a double-bind situation, with him close enough for her to smell the tangy scent of his aftershave... feel the undeniable magnetism of his personality. Working together, his hands brushing hers from time to time, brought a sense of unnerving awareness that made it difficult to even think straight.

This charming front is deliberate, you fool, she told herself grimly, but it didn't help.

The rain beat against the tall window, seeming to match the hasty rhythm of her heart.

'There's a right old storm blowing up,' Mike observed with a frown. He eyed her with what might have been a gleam of mischief. 'Are you afraid of thunder and lightning?'

'No. Of course not,' she denied tightly, repressing a shudder as a loud retort rent the air.

'Pity,' he said coolly. 'I suppose it's too much to expect you to admit to a little vulnerability.'

Laura glared. 'Does my independence threaten you, Mr Brady?'

'Not at all. I like it.' He moved closer. 'But think what you're missing. If you were afraid, I might have to put my arms about you.'

She snorted inelegantly. 'I shouldn't have thought you were the kind of man who needed excuses.'

'I don't.' He met her challenging look with a hard stare, and reached for her.

She dodged away, made nervous by the narrow, intent expression. 'I'm here to work,' she reminded him sharply, 'not to provide you with a little light entertainment.' Nor with the means of revenge, she added in silent bitterness.

'Is that what you think I'm after?'

He was close enough now for her to feel the warmth of his body, but he didn't touch her. She stepped back a pace. 'I don't know . . . nor do I care.'

There was a tremor in her voice, Laura noted in disgust. What was it about this man that reduced her to a helpless jelly?

'And I should keep your romantic attentions where they belong,' she said on a surge of frustrated fury. 'Then your fiancée wouldn't need to find her own diversions.'

His face grew still, and Laura gasped, her hands flying to her cheeks, which were hot with dismay. What on earth had possessed her to blurt that out in that childish way?

'Meaning?' he asked coolly.

'Nothing. I'm sorry.' Laura bit her lip helplessly. 'It's not my business.'

'You seem to be making it your business.' He gripped her chin suddenly, forcing her eyes up to his. 'Are you bothered by the thought of my marrying Marietta?'

'Don't be ridiculous.' Laura's breathing was ragged. Why did his smallest touch elicit an almost instant response? she wondered in irritation. 'Why should I be bothered?'

He gave her a thin smile. 'An intriguing question, and one I'd like an answer to.'

She tore her head away from his grasp, unable to go on looking into those disturbingly perceptive eyes.

'You can draw your own conclusions. It doesn't mean they're right.' She began to put her things together. 'It's obvious you didn't really come to help me get this job done,' she accused tightly. 'Never mind. From the measurements I've taken I know which set of figures is the accurate one.' She snapped her small case shut. 'I'll find my own way out. Goodbye.'

She turned to go, but he caught her arm fiercely. 'When are you going to stop lying to yourself, Laura, and face up to things the way they really are?'

'By which you mean the way you want them to be.'

He nodded. 'The way *you* want them too.'

He bent to kiss her, but she pulled sharply away. 'This is all a game to you, isn't it, Mike Brady?'

'Is it? Are you sure?'

His eyes were full of a subtle light, which shone into her own, dazzling her senses. Suddenly, she was sure of nothing.

'Why are you doing this?' she demanded in a low, furious voice. 'Don't you feel any loyalty at all to the woman you're going to marry?'

'Do you mean Marietta?' His mouth curved into a cynical smile. 'She knows the score.'

Laura stared at him, outraged. Were all men the same? Did they all treat fidelity so lightly? 'I'm sure she does,' she said scornfully.

His hands gripped her shoulders like bands of steel. 'And if I wasn't going to marry her? What then?'

'But you are,' Laura insisted. 'And I'm marrying Hubert in a few weeks' time.'

He thrust his face into hers. 'Are you still determined to make that foolish mistake?'

'My only recent mistake has been to take this job for you,' she bit back furiously. 'And now I wish to heaven I had never agreed to do it.'

'I'm sure you do.' He shook her roughly. 'That way you could have gone stubbornly into marriage with a man you don't love and who doesn't love you.'

'How are you suddenly such an expert on my life?' she demanded jeeringly.

'I don't need to be an expert to know Laine is wrong for you . . . and for Joe.'

'Leave Joe out of this.' Tears of fury stung Laura's eyes. 'He's my son and I know what's best for him.'

'That's obvious.' Mike gave a sharp, humourless laugh. 'Out of fear, you'll take him from one impossible situation and dump him into another that's even worse.'

'That's only your opinion, Mike Brady. Hubert will learn to love Joe——'

'I doubt it,' he cut in harshly. 'Any more than you'll learn to love Laine.' He drew her roughly against him. 'But then, you wouldn't know love if it was staring you in the face, would you, Laura?'

He was glaring at her with narrow-eyed intensity, and she felt the tremor grow into visible shaking.

'Let go of me,' she commanded breathlessly, as a dreadful weakness began to overtake her.

'I don't want to, Laura,' he said, his voice low and insistent. 'And you don't want me to, I know.'

He kissed her then, his mouth a sweet invasion, smothering her protesting cry, moving exultantly as he felt her resistance ebbing away. She had no strength left for resistance now; her hands clung to him in a kind of desperation, which he met by folding her more closely into his embrace.

She could feel the tension in him, a kind of hunger which she recognised because she shared it. No kiss, however sweet, however enveloping, could assuage the peculiar ache which penetrated every part of her.

Crushed against his hard body, she knew a primitive urge to possess him, to be possessed by him—an urge so intense that it seemed to sap her will. She arched her body against him, begging unashamedly for him to take her, and heard him groan.

Slowly, he lifted his head. 'Not here, Laura. Not now.'

His words were a dash of cold water. 'Oh, God!' she cried, her breath ragged in her throat. 'What am I doing?'

He wanted her, but not here. Not in the house he intended to share with Marietta. Hot humiliation flowed through her as she struggled to disentangle herself.

'Let me go!'

'Calm down.' He released her slowly. 'There's no need to panic, Laura.' His breathing was as short and uneven as her own, she noted with a kind of pained satisfaction. The surrender hadn't all been on her side.

'I'm not panicking.' Laura was surprised by the steadiness of her voice. 'In fact, I've just regained my common sense.'

He shook his head at her.

'Don't do it, Laura.' The lines of his face were grim. 'Don't try to reason away what has nothing to do with reason.'

'I'll choose my own thinking, thank you,' she retorted tautly. 'And now I'm really going.'

'I'll drop you home in my car,' he said resignedly, as she picked up her briefcase. 'The weather's too bad for you to drive.'

'Don't be ridiculous. I'm perfectly capable of driving in a storm. I'm not helpless.'

'No. Just stubborn and foolish.'

'Thanks for your opinion. But I wonder who's really the fool?'

He stared at her for what seemed an endless time before he conceded wearily, 'You know, you could be right, at that.'

The rain was absolutely torrential. Laura, with the windscreen-wipers on at their fastest speed, had difficulty seeing out through the curtain of water which poured down the screen. It was terrifying, though wild horses wouldn't have dragged that admission from her. On strange, narrow roads, with the possibility of traffic appearing suddenly around every bend, it was ridiculous to go on, but there seemed no alternative. She could hardly just stop here and wait for the storm to abate. It was obvious from the sky that this weather was in for the night.

Laura bit her lip, wishing her pride hadn't forced her to turn down Mike Brady's offer to drive her. She had thought she could manage, but then she hadn't bargained for the ferocity of the storm. If she drove slowly for the next few miles, she knew she would eventually find herself on the motorway. But she had no way of knowing whether conditions would be better there, or worse.

A flash of lightning and a momentary lull in the wind-blown rain cleared the screen enough for her to see ahead. What she saw brought her to an abrupt halt. There was a police car ahead, its blue light flashing a warning.

Laura opened her side-window as a shape loomed there.

'You can't go on, I'm afraid.' A policeman, with a river of water running from his hat, looked in at her. 'The road ahead has subsided, which means you'll have to take a detour. But if I were you I'd give up and go back home.'

'But I don't live locally,' Laura protested. 'I'm trying to get back to town.'

He shook his head, soaking her with droplets from his hat. 'You won't do it this way. The detour will add miles to your journey, and there have already been a couple of accidents on the motorway.' He pointed to a side-road just ahead. 'There's a hotel up that way. I'd advise you to book in there for the night. Trying to get home in this isn't worth the risk.'

Beside which, I'd probably get lost in the narrow lanes, Laura admitted in silent gloom. Just for once, she would have to admit defeat and take the easy way out.

'Thank you, Officer,' she said. 'Is the hotel very far down the road?'

'About half a mile,' he told her, straightening up. 'You can't miss it.'

He was right. The small country hotel was a blaze of lights, visible as a bright blur through the rain-drenched windscreen, and, with a sigh of relief, Laura turned off the road into the wide front drive, coming to a halt at the entrance.

A uniformed man was there, with a large umbrella and a welcoming smile. Laura thought sourly that it was an ill wind that brought nobody any good. The hotel would probably profit from the atrocious weather conditions, since there was bound to be more than one marooned motorist seeking shelter there.

'There's no need for you to get wet, madam. If you'll give me the keys, I'll park the car for you.'

'Oh, thanks.'

Laura allowed him to escort her up the shallow flight of steps, under shelter of his umbrella, and into the reception lobby.

'Welcome.' The receptionist smiled.

'A single room, please,' Laura requested, adding with a smile, 'That is, if you're not fully booked.'

'Almost, but we can squeeze you in,' the girl assured her. 'Do you want dinner?'

'Probably. But what I'd really like is a nice hot bath.'

'The only room we have en suite is a double, I'm afraid.' The girl shook her head regretfully. 'If you take the single, there's a shared bathroom on the landing, but you may have to queue.'

'I'll take the double, thanks,' Laura said decisively. She was in no mood for company, and particularly not in a queue for the bath.

While the bath-water was running, Laura telephoned Florence to explain her predicament. 'Hopefully, the storm will have blown over by the morning and I'll be able to get back,' she said, trying to keep the doubt out of her voice.

She spoke to Joe, and felt a little ache in the region of her heart at the sound of his clear, high voice. He was still little more than a baby.

In the bath, she thought about what had happened at Gladstone House. If it was revenge Mike Brady was seeking, she thought, he'd achieved it. The sensations of being in his arms would probably haunt her for a lifetime.

And the things he'd said tormented her. She couldn't deny to herself that he'd voiced some of her own fears, which had grown in the face of what had happened when she'd last seen Hubert. Perhaps it was pre-wedding jitters, but if it wasn't . . . then she might be in for more than she'd bargained for when she'd accepted his proposal.

And it was no safer to let her mind dwell on Mike Brady than on her impending marriage.

Impatiently, she got out of the bath. It was clear her mind intended to give her no peace to enjoy it.

The hotel was small and comfortable, with a homely feel about it. The dining-room was almost full, but the waiter found her a single table. Laura ordered home-made steak and kidney pie with fresh vegetables, but she was still too wound up to do it justice.

Walking back to her room, she decided to go to bed early and make an early start in the morning. She was on the point of fitting her key into the door, when it opened from inside.

'Hello, Laura!' Mike Brady stood there, with a towel wrapped about his middle. 'Come in and shut the door. It's a little public out here for my present *déshabillé* state.'

Laura stared at him, open-mouthed. 'What on earth are you doing in my room?'

'Having a bath.' He pulled her impatiently inside and shut the door. 'At least, I was. I've finished now.'

'Let me rephrase the question.' Laura folded her lips in annoyance. 'Why are you taking a bath in *my* room instead of in your own?'

'Because I don't have a room,' he said reasonably, his blue eyes resting calmly on her face. 'There wasn't a room available. The hotel is full.'

He moved across to a trolley, which Laura suddenly noticed was laid for a meal.

'I'm very hungry,' he said by way of explanation.

'Who let you in?' she persisted, ignoring his plea for sympathy.

'The receptionist.' He sounded pleased with himself. 'Luckily I noticed you'd already signed into a double room, so I just added my name to your reservation.'

'What?' Laura cried incredulously. 'You added your name to mine on the register?'

He laughed at her expression. 'Well, perhaps "add" is the wrong word. What I actually did was alter it a little.'

Laura's temper began to flare. 'You had no right to add or alter. How dare you?'

'Who dares wins,' he answered stirringly. 'I was wet, cold and hungry, and there was no room at the inn, except for half of yours. All things being equal, I didn't think you'd want me thrust back out into the storm.'

'I hate to dampen your optimism,' Laura said grimly. 'But you are not staying here. I'm practically a married woman——'

'Practically, but not quite,' he cut in. 'And I'm here to share your room, not your bed. I won't lay a single finger on you, I promise—Scout's honour.'

Laura smiled thinly. 'If you were ever in the Scouts I'd be willing to bet you were drummed out. And as for honour, how did you *honourably* get the hotel to let you into my room?'

'It was rather good, actually. I saw your signature in the register, and told the receptionist you were my wife, who'd come on ahead of me. I told her we had only recently got married and you had a terrible memory when it came to your new name. Nice girl, that receptionist. She was very sympathetic, and sportingly allowed me to correct your mistake.'

'"Nice girl"!' Laura cried hotly. 'You probably drowned the poor thing in those wonderful blue eyes of yours. She must have been positively besotted to let you tamper with the register.'

'Oh, I did it very discreetly,' he said nonchalantly. 'All we have to do is remember to answer to the name of Mr and Mrs Maxwell-Brady.' He moved towards her, smiling in a pleased way. 'Could someone really drown in my eyes?'

'This is ridiculous,' Laura exclaimed tightly, and crossed to the telephone. 'I'm going to ring Reception and have you thrown out.'

'Like this?' He grinned at her and discarded his towel.

Laura's eyes closed in instant and automatic reaction, and she heard his deep, amused laugh. Furious, she opened them again to find that he was wearing a pair of white briefs, which did nothing to hide the contours of his body, but did preserve a modicum of modesty.

'Very amusing,' she said in dry annoyance. 'But I'd still have had you thrown out even if you had been stark naked.'

'Reception.' A disembodied voice spoke in her ear.

'Thank you, this is——'

The receiver was deftly retrieved from her grasp, and Mike's free hand came across her shoulder to cover her mouth.

'Mr and Mrs Maxwell-Brady in room 227, and we'd like a bottle of champagne,' he said pleasantly. 'Your best.'

He released his hand from her mouth and, as she turned furiously to face him, he replaced it with his lips, smothering her protests in a warm, sweet kiss. She was flushed and breathless by the time he lifted his head.

'That was just to stop you saying something you'd be sorry for.' He stepped back from her. 'Hands off I promised, and hands off it will be.' He smiled at her slyly. 'Unless you make the first move.'

Laura said coldly, 'Then hands off it will definitely remain.'

He sighed. 'I wish I had your iron control.'

'It's easy. Try remembering that we're both engaged to be married,' Laura advised, adding sourly, 'That should douse any flames of passion which might inadvertently arise.'

'There'd be nothing inadvertent about it.' His rich laugh filled the room, sending a *frisson* of pleasure up Laura's spine. He really did have a wonderful voice. 'If you don't want to eat, come and sit with me while I do. There's a little matter I'd like to straighten out.'

Unwillingly, Laura sat in the chair opposite to him at the little table set in the window. He shouldn't be here, and soon she would have to think of a way to get rid of him, but there was something in the subtly commanding tone of his voice that warned her he was serious beneath the teasing.

'Is it something to do with with the house?' she asked, with a touch of sudden anxiety.

'Indirectly.' He transferred food from the hot dishes on to a plate and tasted some before looking up. 'What gave you the idea that I was going to marry Marietta?'

Taken by surprise, Laura blinked several times before her brain could formulate an answer. 'Well, I seem to remember you saying...' She paused, frowning in an effort to remember, and disconcerted by his raised brows. 'Didn't you tell me you were to be married soon?'

'That I might have done. But did I mention Marietta?'

Laura shook her head in faint annoyance. 'She was with you at the party, holding your hand, her eyes warning me off; I suppose I just assumed...'

'She had no right.' He smiled. 'And are you always that easily warned off?'

Laura shrugged irritably, beginning, for some reason, to feel a little foolish. 'I don't know. I can't say I've had the experience before. Besides, I'm not in competition for you.'

'True. There's no competition.' Mike's voice was curiously low, making her look at him more closely. He returned her scrutiny with a look that made her blood race in her veins, and she turned her gaze hastily away.

'I'm glad you agree!' she said, aware of a hollow sensation in the pit of her stomach. She had a feeling she would regret prolonging this conversation, but had to go on. 'Do you mean you've called the wedding off?'

'I haven't,' he replied, deliberately abstruse.

'Do you mean *she* has?' she asked disbelievingly. 'Then why was Marietta choosing furnishings with you at Designers' Choice?' Adding hurriedly, as she saw his expression, 'I saw you both outside the store the other day, and she was obviously choosing something.'

'Yes. Her wedding present.' He laughed at the vexed look on her face. 'She's marrying Brian Huxley.'

Laura stared at him, speechless, and then a picture appeared in her mind's eye of Marietta and Brian together at the restaurant, oblivious to everyone but each other.

'On the rebound?' she asked faintly.

'No. Quite by choice. I was only introduced to her at the engagement party.'

'Then why the possessiveness about you?'

'A little of the dog in the manger, perhaps,' he laughed. 'But that's just Marietta.'

Laura licked at lips that had suddenly gone dry. 'Well, if it's not Marietta, then who are you marrying?'

He grinned. 'One day soon I'll tell you.'

'Don't bother,' she shrugged, and turned away. 'All this is really none of my business.'

She went to the window and stared out at the torrential rain lashing in gusts against the tall trees in the hotel garden. They seemed to be straining at the roots. She started backwards as a brilliant flash of lightning stabbed through the sky towards the window.

'I think this is the worst storm I've ever seen,' she observed in a voice that wobbled a bit.

'If you're frightened, we could always cuddle up together.'

His voice was close to her ear, and she turned, startled, to look into his deep blue gaze.

'You never give up, do you?' She moved quickly away.

'Not easily, no.' He moved towards her again and, with a flash of panic, Laura thought that he was stalking her.

Desperately, she looked around the room for a means of escape, and realised something that hadn't penetrated her hazy mind before. 'There's only one bed.'

'Yes,' he said, deliberately offhand. 'Looks like we'll have to toss for it.'

'Oh, no, we won't,' Laura argued hotly. 'I had this room first and this is my bed.' She looked doubtfully at the two rather small armchairs. It was impossible to imagine how, even put together, they could accommodate his tall frame. 'If you can't make something comfortable out of those, you'll probably have to sleep in the bath; it's quite a big one, and there are plenty of nice thick towels.'

'Oh, well.' Mike shrugged despairingly. 'At least you're not still threatening to have me thrown out.'

'Now I've seen the height of the storm, I don't think my conscience would allow it,' she said, adding with a touch of dry humour, 'All I hope is that my mother never gets to hear of this.'

'What's it worth to make sure she doesn't hear of it from me?' He narrowed his eyes in a mock-menacing smile.

'Absolutely nothing!' Laura felt strangely light-hearted, considering the circumstances. 'Since she'll never allow you anywhere near enough to tell her.'

'Hmm,' he said consideringly. 'I didn't think she'd taken to me somehow.'

Laura laughed. 'That's an understatement.'

'Pity——' he shook his head '—because your father quite likes me.'

Laura frowned at him, confused by an echo of his words which rang in her head in her father's quiet voice. She was about to question him on his remark, but decided it would only make the present situation even more ludicrous.

'I'm tired, and I want to make an early start for home tomorrow; so if you'll excuse me I'll go to bed.' She pulled a blanket from the bed, and handed him a pillow. 'I'll be using the bathroom for a minute or two, but after that it's all yours.'

'Thanks.' He smiled sardonically. 'If I keep my hands behind my back, do I get a goodnight kiss?'

'I think not.' Laura darted away from him before she could succumb to the invitation lurking in the depths of those dangerous blue eyes.

CHAPTER SEVEN

BANSHEES were howling outside Laura's door and the walls of the room seemed to be creaking under a great weight. As the creaking became a groan, the walls began to fall in.

Laura screamed and tried to scramble to her feet as something heavy crashed near by, but her hands and feet were inexplicably tied. She screamed again.

'Laura! Stop it! You're all right.'

Laura's eyes opened. 'Why have you tied me up?' She gasped. 'Let me go.'

'Calm down, keep still, and I will.' Mike's blue eyes were looking into hers with a mixture of exasperation and sympathy. 'You've been dreaming, and you're all tangled up in the sheets.'

'But the walls fell,' she said, coming awake only slowly. 'There was a terrible noise.'

'Yes, I know.' His voice was soothing. 'A tree's gone down outside, but we're in no danger.'

He unwrapped her gently from the restraining sheet and sat her up on the edge of the bed. 'Stay put while I find out what damage has been done.'

'Don't leave me yet.' Wide awake now, Laura had begun to tremble. 'Give me a minute to recover my nerve.'

'Take all the time you want.' He sat beside her and put his arm about her shoulders, drawing her head into the hollow of his throat.

Laura heard the forceful beat of his heart hammering away, and looked up. 'It sounds as though you had a shock too,' she said. Somehow it made her feel better. He was human after all.

'That's putting it mildly,' he smiled. 'I was sleeping when the noise woke me with a terrible start. I don't know whether to worry about the lump on my head or the hole in the bath.'

Laura laughed shakily and sat up. 'As long as I'm not expected to pay for the damage!'

'Are you all right now?' he asked, and she nodded.

Putting her gently from him, he stood up and went to the window. Laura crossed to join him. The fact that she was in her slip and pants in lieu of a nightdress and he was wearing only the white briefs seemed neither here nor there.

The outside lights were on, and they could see that two huge trees had gone down into the car park, crushing a number of vehicles. It was a scene of devastation. In the pouring rain, figures were already moving about.

'Oh, lord!' Laura said. 'I hope my car's not under that lot.'

'Nor mine.' Mike left the window and began shrugging hastily into his clothes. 'I'll go down and find out.'

'I'll come with you,' Laura said determinedly.

'There's no need for us both to get drenched. Stay here! I'll come back as soon as I find out anything.'

She protested as she followed him to the door, but he was adamant, thrusting her back into the room as people began to spill into the corridor outside.

'You're not dressed for company,' he pointed out, and pulled the door almost shut.

A woman was shrieking somewhere among the hubbub.

'I'm afraid my—er—wife's a little hysterical,' a man's anxious voice said. 'What's happened?'

Listening through the half-open door, Laura thought the voice sounded familiar, and wondered if she was a little hysterical herself.

'Trees down,' she heard Mike say. 'In the car park. I'm just going to find out——'

He broke off as other voices were raised, and the room door was pulled to with a slam, leaving Laura alone and consumed with frustrated curiosity. She rushed to the wardrobe to get her clothes. The door opened again just as she was buttoning up her dress, and Mike's face, looking surprisingly grim, appeared around it.

'Where do you think you're going?' he demanded.

'Downstairs, to see what's going on.' Laura pulled on her shoes and stood up to face him. 'I don't see why I should miss all the excitement, just because you want to play Macho Man!'

'The storm isn't over,' he told her irritably. 'And there are a lot of trees around this place that could fall any minute. The last thing I want now is the problem of how to get you to hospital on a night like this with no direct road out.' He grabbed her arm and pushed her towards the bed. 'Sit there and wait, or I really will tie you up.'

Left alone again, Laura fumed. He was an arrogant, domineering brute of a man, she told herself furiously, but, as she began to calm down, the sense of what he'd said began to penetrate. She could well imagine Florence's face on receiving the news that her daughter had had to be carted off to hospital in the middle of the night, having spent the first half of it sleeping in the same room as Mike Brady.

No. As much as she wanted to assert herself against his overbearing behaviour, she would be better off waiting here for him.

She spent the time peering through the window, trying to make order out of the chaos below. The car nearest to the base of the tree seemed to be the same shade of red as her car, in the dim light, and, with a sinking heart, she tried to read the registration number, but it was impossible from the window, and there was no point in guessing.

Mike was gone twenty minutes, and she'd half decided to go downstairs, despite his orders, when he returned. 'Bad news, I'm afraid,' he said. 'Your car's a write-off and mine is undriveable but can probably be restored eventually.'

Laura let out her breath in a long groan. 'Oh, great! Just what I need now. No car.'

'It's hardly the end of the world. The car's insured, isn't it?' His tone was brusque and Laura looked at him in surprise. His face was unnaturally suffused with colour and his brows were lowered in a deep frown.

'Well, it wouldn't hurt to show a little sympathy,' she said tightly. 'Of course the car's insured, but goodness knows how long it will be before it's replaced, and I need a car for my business.'

'The only job you've got time for at the moment is mine,' he argued. 'And if you need to get around for that, I don't mind chauffering you.'

'In your ruined car?' Her voice rose sarcastically.

'I have another.'

'I wish I were as lucky!' Laura's chest swelled with fury. 'Believe it or not, I do have a life outside of the work I'm doing for you, and I resent your attitude.'

'I'm sorry.' He took her hand and patted it. 'I'm just trying to plan ahead for tomorrow. With both cars out of action, we're virtually marooned here.'

To her surprise, he sat down suddenly in the armchair and put his head in his hands, rubbing his fingers against his eyes.

'"Marooned"?' Laura repeated. 'This is hardly a desert island.'

'It might as well be,' he replied tersely. 'Apparently, this weather is forecast to go on for a while longer yet, which will certainly complicate matters.' He stood up. 'Well. There's nothing we can do for the moment, except get some rest.' He gave a resigned sigh. 'So it's back to the bath.' He rubbed at his neck. 'By tomorrow I'll have a permanent crick.'

Laura looked at him guiltily. 'Is it that bad? I thought it was quite a big bath.'

'So it would be,' he agreed wryly, 'for someone your size. For me it's somewhat inadequate.' He glanced longingly at the bed. 'I don't suppose you'd be willing to swap?'

'No, I wouldn't!' she snapped. 'I was here first.'

He shrugged his broad shoulders. 'It was worth a try. I suppose I should just be grateful you didn't insist on getting me thrown out. Otherwise, I might have decided to sleep in the car and I'd have had more than a crick in my neck to worry about now.'

'Oh, don't.' Laura shuddered. 'I can't bear to think about it.'

He paused to look at her. 'Do you mean it bothers you?' His eyes glinted. 'Things are looking up.'

'Of course it bothers me,' she muttered, her heart beating unevenly as his gaze continued to hold hers. 'You're a human being, aren't you?'

'Just about.' His mouth twisted ironically. 'And thanks for your concern.'

'Don't mention it.'

He looked again at the bed. 'We could always put some pillows down the middle,' he suggested hopefully. 'And I'd keep my promise. Scout's honour... remember?' He raised two fingers against his temple in a chaste salute. 'And if you swear on Guide's honour, we should both be safe enough.'

'I was never a Guide.' Laura fought to repress a smile. 'And your virtue is as safe as houses with me.'

'What a depressing thought,' he said dourly. 'I must be losing my charisma.'

Laura turned hastily away. If he saw her face, he would know that he wasn't. His warm vitality seemed to fill the room.

And later, as she lay in solitary splendour, the knowledge that he was there, in the next room, created a heat which warmed her chill body, and brought a disturbing excitement which kept her awake. She thought she could hear the soft, even rhythm of his breathing, and feel its strangely disturbing vibration.

She was awake before him. He was still sleeping soundly as she tiptoed into the bathroom to clean her teeth. He was right, she thought, pausing to look down at him, the bath was far too cramped for his large frame. His arms and legs lay in distorted positions, and she guessed he would be aching all over when he finally got up.

His face was turned away from her, exposing the strong contour of the side of his neck. For some reason, it was a compellingly erotic sight, which had her battling against an urge to press her lips against the firm, warm skin.

Lord, I must be mad! she thought shakily, dragging herself away from the ridiculous temptation. What was it about this man that made him so magnetically attractive?

She crept back to bed and lay there, waiting for him to wake up and trying to sort out the subtle change in her feelings about him. Did it have anything to do with the fact that he wasn't going to marry Marietta? But that was silly. He was still going to marry someone. What did it matter whether she could put a name to the girl or not?

The telephone rang close to her head, startling her heart into a rapid tattoo. How many more shocks was she expected to withstand? she wondered shakily as she lifted the receiver.

'Good morning, madam,' a girl's voice spoke. 'I'm ringing to enquire about your welfare and to apologise for any disruption caused by the storm last night. Are you and Mr Maxwell-Brady all right?'

'I—er—Mr Maxwell-Brady and I are...fine, thank you,' Laura said, almost choking over the double-barrelled name.

'Oh, good. I have a note here that your cars were damaged. Would you like to call in at Reception, at your convenience, to discuss the matter?'

'Yes, of course,' Laura said, as Mike came sleepily into the room. He slumped down on the bed beside her as she replaced the receiver.

'That was Reception,' she explained, wishing he hadn't chosen to sit so close. 'They want to see us about the damage to our cars.'

He groaned, and leaned back against the pillows. 'So it wasn't a nightmare?'

'No. I'm afraid not.'

His arm came across her as he stretched and flexed his muscles. The touch of his body against hers was creating a fire inside her, and she tried delicately to extricate herself.

'I must get up.'

'What's the hurry?' His voice was low and still husky from sleep.

'I'd like to get the business of my car sorted out.'

'It'll keep.'

He dipped his head unexpectedly to brush his lips against the side of her throat.

She jerked away. 'Remember your promise,' she said a little unevenly. 'Last night you promised to keep your hands off.'

'That was last night,' he murmured against her skin. 'Today is a whole new day.'

'Mike,' she said, hating the pleading note in her voice, 'don't.'

'You didn't say that yesterday... at the house.'

Laura squirmed. If she'd hoped he'd been unaware of the signals she'd been sending him then, her hopes were dashed now. He'd known how much she'd wanted him.

'As you said, that was yesterday.' She tried to pull away, but his arm clamped firmly about her shoulder. And, as she struggled in vain, she grew angry. 'And, as I recall, it was you who became just a little reluctant.'

She'd hoped to disconcert him into loosening his hold, but he only raised his eyebrows. 'And what interpretation did you put on my reluctance?'

She gave a short, bitter laugh. 'That you obviously didn't want to sully your marriage home with the furtive gropings of lust,' she said thickly, wondering why her eyes filled with sudden tears.

To her consternation, he pulled her down on to the bed and put his arms more firmly about her.

'So, you admit it? You were lusting after my body!'

'Nothing of the sort. I meant your lust, not mine!' she argued, struggling against an almost overwhelming desire to snuggle up to him and let everything and everyone go hang. But there was something she had to know.

'If you're not going to marry Marietta, then for whom are you keeping the house sacred?'

'What a poetic mind you have, Laura. I like it.' Mike nibbled at her earlobe, sending her rigid with the tingling sensations that were running down her spine. 'But my reluctance had nothing to do with the house, and everything to do with you and me. In my view, an empty room and a dusty floor was no place for our love affair to begin. I wanted our first time together to be somewhere where I could give you my full and undivided attention. Like now.'

Laura's struggles increased, fuelled by his certainty that there would be a first time.

But he held her firmly, his tongue outlining her ear, distracting her from her anger and driving her into a fatal mistake. She turned in his arms to face him, and knew it was a wrong move as soon as she saw his expression. He was smiling like a cat who had just trapped the canary.

'I told myself you were worth waiting for, Laura,' he murmured. 'But fate seems to be telling me there's no time like the present.'

She wanted to ask what he meant, but his lips covered hers, making speech impossible. His tongue tantalised the contours of her soft mouth, before entering to touch, with incredible sensuality, against her own. His hands, moving like silk against her burning skin, beckoned her on, melting her bones along with her resistance.

Laura shuddered, unable to control her response. She clung to him, returning kiss for burning kiss... caress for sensuous caress. When he lifted his head, she felt as though she were being torn in two.

He was leaning over her, his eyes looking down into hers with a strangely intense expression.

'There's something I've got to know, Laura.' The words seemed to catch in his throat. 'You... and... Hubert Laine. Have you slept with him?'

Laura stared at him, filled with revulsion, which quickly doused the passion that had been building within her. Why did he have to talk about Hubert in the middle of making love to her?

'That's my business,' she snapped furiously. 'And if you were hoping to turn me off stone cold, then you've succeeded.'

She began to struggle out of his grasp, but he held her firmly, cupping her chin in his hands almost painfully to prevent her looking away.

'Please, Laura,' he said, and she guessed it was the nearest he'd ever come to pleading. 'This is important to me.'

'I can't think why it should be,' she returned irritably, and then, as he continued to hold her gaze, 'No. As a matter of fact I haven't. Does that satisfy your curiosity?'

He groaned and gathered her close again, the thrust of his tongue now suddenly fierce, the movement of his hands over her body possessively arousing. She made no protest as he stripped her underclothes swiftly away, only clinging more tightly as his lips slid down her arched throat to her breasts. His hands caressed the taut swell of her stomach, the aching softness of her inner thighs. The sensations his touch evoked were exquisite torture, and she moaned faintly.

He brought his mouth again to hers, kissing her with devastating gentleness growing to passionate intensity as she met him every step of the way with her own demands. He moved to draw her even closer, and Laura gasped at the hard, urgent pressure of his body against hers, the sound bringing her back to the edge of sanity. In a second or two it would be too late, her mind warned desperately and, mustering the tattered remnants of her self-control, she tore her mouth from his.

His eyes opened and looked into hers, soundlessly questioning, trying to demolish her defences...to burn away her final reluctance with a searing blue flame.

'It's no good, Mike,' she whispered raggedly. 'I can't.'

He drew a sharp, inward breath. 'Can't? Or won't?'

She shook her head and said on a note of finality, 'Either way, it's the same.'

He levered himself away and stood up, and Laura gasped at the sight of his taut, muscular body as he bent to recover his briefs.

'That damned integrity of yours!' he said tightly, meeting her eyes with narrow intensity. 'I only wish Laine was worth your keeping it.'

Laura sat up, pulling the sheet hastily up about her bare breasts. 'You obviously think you're worth my losing it!'

He met her indignant glare with ice-blue eyes. 'And you obviously think I'm not.'

Laura shook her head helplessly, but he had turned away and was walking into the bathroom. He shut the door behind him with a snap. She turned her head into the pillow and wept hot, silent tears. Her heart ached with a peculiar sense of loss.

She must have slept. When she woke, Mike was standing at the window, fully dressed. There were sounds of activity from outside, and she guessed someone was trying to remove the trees from the crushed cars.

But she wasn't thinking of the cars at that moment; her eyes were on Mike, taking in the broad sweep of his shoulders, the taut muscularity of his thighs and legs in the well-fitting trousers. A shudder ran through her at the memory of sensations that exciting body had aroused.

Never before had she felt such a fever in the blood . . . a blind need that only total surrender to this one man could assuage. She sighed, and he turned.

'Ah! You're awake!' he said matter-of-factly.

'Just about.' Laura's voice was husky.

He was looking down at her with a slight frown, his eyes guarded, but seeming to seek something from her own. She returned his look with the same wariness, hiding the thrill of meeting that brilliant blue gaze behind a frown.

'What time is it?' she asked.

'Time we were trying to get out of this mess.'

He went back to the window, giving her the moment of privacy she needed to slip out of bed and retrieve her discarded underclothes. She wanted a bath, but thought, in the circumstances, it might be better to settle for a shower.

Mike turned just as she was getting into her bra, and she fumbled with the catch. It slipped to reveal her breast, and she grabbed it hastily.

He gave her a cynical little smile that she had no trouble interpreting. Only a little while ago, she'd been stark naked in his arms and there wasn't one inch of her body he hadn't explored. This little act of modesty was like shutting the stable door after the horse had bolted.

'I won't be long,' she said, and escaped to the bathroom.

When she came out again some time later he wasn't there, but he returned within moments, wearing a look of decisiveness which lifted Laura's spirits.

'Have you thought of a way to get home?' she asked hopefully.

'Yes and no,' he said obscurely. 'It all depends.'

'On what?' Laura snapped, annoyed by his evasion.

'On whether I can arrange something.'

Laura felt a sharp stab of annoyance. 'I'm sure you'll manage something. Meanwhile, I'll stay here. I'll be quite happy to have this room to myself. When conditions improve, I assume there'll be some form of public transport?'

'I wouldn't bank on it.' He laughed sourly. 'Besides, this place isn't safe. If I'd known how many trees there were, and in what close proximity they stood to practically every part of the hotel, I'd have been a great deal more worried.'

'Then perhaps it's just as well you didn't know,' she said coolly. 'But we know now...and it is worrying. But what's the alternative?'

'Get your things together,' he ordered brusquely. 'There'll be transport downstairs in a few minutes.'

'But I thought you said the roads were very bad,' Laura argued as she put on her coat.

He nodded. 'They are, but we'll manage the short distance we're going.'

He took her arm, but she shrugged away. 'I must telephone my parents to let Joe know I'm trying to get home. Will we get there today?'

'It's possible,' he shrugged, 'but unlikely. As I said, it depends.' And, as she opened her mouth for another question, he ushered her towards the phone.

'Make that call,' he commanded. 'I'll come back for you in a minute.'

'Don't bother,' she snapped. 'I think I can find my way to the lobby.'

He didn't answer. He left the room quickly as she lifted the receiver. He was back just as she was putting it down again.

'OK?' he queried, and, without waiting for an answer, he grasped her elbow and ushered her to the door. He opened it and popped his head out to survey the corridor before indicating with a nod of his head that she should go out.

'Is the coast clear?' she said sarcastically, feeling as though she'd been catapulted into some kind of third-rate thriller movie.

'It had better be,' he replied grimly as he led her down the corridor.

'But where are we going?' she insisted irritably.

Ignoring her query, and the lift, he led her on down the two flights of stairs to Reception, passing the desk without pause.

'But the cars . . .' Laura said, hanging back a little.

'All taken care of,' he assured her firmly, guiding her out through the front entrance. 'Well, at least the rain's stopped,' he observed with a grimace of satisfaction. 'That should make things a little easier.'

At the foot of the steps stood two horses, saddled and ready, and held by a lad in porter's uniform.

'Oh, by the way,' Mike said, 'I forgot to ask if you could ride.'

CHAPTER EIGHT

THE morning was blustery, with huge rainclouds chasing swiftly across a still ominous sky. The violent hand of the storm was apparent everywhere as they picked their way along. The fields on low-lying ground were flooded and storm-felled trees were strewn everywhere.

On the hilly track, where Laura rode beside Mike, the water had begun to drain down, but the ground was soft and difficult beneath the horses' feet. If she'd had a sneaking feeling that she'd like to turn the horse's head towards home, she knew now it would be impossible to make it over the long distance.

'Do you think you could now tell me where we're headed?' Laura asked, a little irritably, breaking the silence that had hung between them.

'To the house of one of my directors,' he informed her shortly, and there was a look of cool amusement in his blue eyes. 'But there will be no one at home, I'm afraid. He and his wife are in Paris at the moment, but if the storm keeps off they might manage to get back with the helicopter some time this afternoon.'

'Oh!' she said a little lamely. 'Why didn't you tell me so earlier?'

'Because I thought the fact that the house would be empty when we got there might have led you to refuse.'

Laura gave a short, unamused laugh. 'It probably would have.'

They went on in silence. Riding in these conditions needed full concentration. Mike leaned towards her from time to time to take hold of her horse's rein to guide it over some hazardous ground. Once or twice Laura felt the brush of his hand against hers, and her insides clenched against even that unintentional contact.

'The going should get easier shortly,' he told her, breaking the silence at last.

'Don't worry about me,' she said stiffly. 'I quite enjoy a challenge.'

'I must remember that,' he replied wryly, flashing her a look that might have been mockery or approval.

They'd been riding for half an hour, when Mike lifted his arm to point at the red-tiled roof visible in a hollow. 'There's the house.'

'Thank goodness,' she murmured. 'I'm simply dying for a cup of tea.'

'And more besides, I should think,' he said. 'I'm beginning to miss my breakfast.'

'I'd just settle for the tea and a chance to get on my feet,' Laura sighed as she followed him down a narrow track.

The house was smaller and more compact than Gladstone House, but none the less it exuded an air of grandeur and the gardens surrounding were beautiful, even in the drenching rain.

Mike dismounted and then made to help Laura down. She brushed his hand away.

'I'm not helpless. I've been riding for years.' She grimaced. 'Just as well, or this ride would really have thrown me in at the deep end.'

He stood back to watch her dismount, his eyebrows rising as she made a bit of a mess of her descent, her skirt rising up to her thighs as it caught against the stirrup.

'I thought you might find it difficult in a skirt,' he commented, his mouth quirking with amusement.

'Well, I'm down now,' Laura snapped. 'Lead on to the kitchen.'

He had a key to the house, which surprised her.

'Do you have access to the homes of all your directors?' she queried wryly, as he led her through a large hallway to the kitchen behind the staircase.

'No,' he said crisply. 'Only this one. Gervaise is also my brother-in-law, married to my sister Charlotte.'

'I see!' Laura was surprised. 'It's hard to imagine you have a sister.'

'And why is that?' His eyes interrogated her coolly, making her hackles rise.

'Well, from your arrogant approach and obvious self-satisfaction I'd never have thought you'd ever had to compete.'

'You're right.' He gave her a cynical smile, as he filled the kettle and plugged it in. 'I've never had to compete with Charlotte—she's always adored me.'

Laura ground her teeth in silent fury. Why did he always seem to have the winning hand? No wonder it bothered him more than most when he had to lose!

'How long are we going to stay here?' she asked, feeling suddenly fretful.

'Not too long, with a bit of luck,' he answered calmly. 'If the water improves a little more, it's possible Gervaise might risk bringing the helicopter back today.'

'Well, let's hope he manages it,' Laura said doubtfully. 'Although I can't say I relish the idea of riding in a helicopter, myself.'

'I thought you said you liked a challenge.' He gave her a cup of tea and sat down beside her with his mug of coffee. His shoulder was close to hers, and she moved away a little. For some reason, nearness to him brought instant heat.

'I do,' she asserted. 'But not an impossible one.'

He laughed. 'You won't have to do a thing but just sit tight. I'll do the rest.'

'Can you fly a helicopter?' Laura couldn't help sounding impressed.

'Of course. I have a full pilot's licence.'

'Of course, I might have known you would,' she replied grimly. 'Why did I bother to ask?'

'Perhaps because you find me fascinating,' he stated with a mocking smile.

She snorted inelegantly. 'That's not exactly how I'd describe my feelings about you.'

'Oh?' His brows rose. 'And just how would you describe them?'

'That's my business,' she said shortly, turning her eyes away from his absorbed gaze. To describe her feelings to him would be impossible, when she couldn't even define them for herself. She stared absently at the window and then gave a sharp cry of annoyance. 'Oh, no! It's raining again.'

Mike scrambled quickly to his feet. 'I'll have to go and put the horses in the stable round the back. Meanwhile, see if you can rustle up something to eat, would you?'

'Yes, oh, master,' Laura gritted, and he laughed.

'You're learning.'

She was making omelettes when he came back drenched to the skin. Laura threw him a towel to mop his dripping hair, and he emerged from its folds looking tousled and youthful, making Laura's heart skip a beat.

'The wind's blowing up again,' he said, sounding irritable. 'And from the look of the sky we're in for another storm.'

'Oh, lord!' Laura bit her lip. 'Does that mean we're going to be stuck here?'

'Probably,' he said, with a cynical smile. 'I can see that doesn't appeal to you. But at least we have the comforts of home.' He peered over her shoulder at the omelette in the pan, his chin grazing her shoulder with an intimacy that had her pulses racing erratically. 'That looks great. When I've eaten, I'll have a nice long soak in the bath.'

'The comforts of home'. The phrase re-echoed in Laura's brain as she washed the dishes a little later. For some reason, it made her feel melancholy, but she knew she wasn't thinking about her spartan little flat.

Mike had lit a log in the living-room grate before going up to the bath, and it was glowing cheerfully as Laura went and sat on the deep-cushioned sofa. If they were going to be marooned together, then it would be hard to find a more pleasant place for it. The lamps lit against the lowering gloom and the flickering flames from the fire seemed to have a calming effect on her nerves.

As Mike had said, this was so much better than being at the hotel. A little frown formed on her brow as she remembered his rush to be gone from there. Had there really been that much risk from falling trees?

Perhaps, she thought uneasily, he'd just wanted to get her on her own at this isolated house. Maybe this was the idyllic setting he'd had in mind for seduction. She steeled herself against the thought. The only way to ensure that didn't happen was to keep him determinedly at arm's length.

And when he came in later, still damp from his bath, and sat down on the sofa beside her, she moved pointedly to an armchair.

Her gesture brought a cynical smile to his face, but he said nothing, simply adjusting his position so that he could stretch out the length of the sofa. He was wearing a short bath-robe, which Laura assumed belonged to Gervaise and which revealed his bare, muscular legs with their fine covering of dark hair.

Laura, sitting opposite to his lithe form, half wished she'd stayed put beside him. It would have been less distracting. 'Do you think Gervaise will come?' she asked, her voice sounding strangely wobbly.

He shrugged. 'It's hardly likely now the weather's changed again. I did try ringing him in Paris before I went into the bath, but there's some interference on the intercontinental lines. Perhaps I'll have better luck later.'

Laura groaned. 'I feel so helpless. Why did I have to go and make the stupid mistake with the window measurements? If I hadn't, none of this would have happened.'

'Quite,' he agreed soberly, but there was a peculiar gleam in his eye that Laura couldn't interpret. 'But since it has happened, why not try to relax and enjoy Charlotte's hospitality? Albeit in her absence. I'm sure she wouldn't mind you making use of anything you want.'

Laura sighed in resignation. 'In that case, perhaps I can use the telephone?'

He shrugged. 'Help yourself.'

She phoned Joe, who was full of his morning's adventures with his kite in the blustery wind. 'But it's come on to rain again,' he announced disgustedly. 'Grandpa said we might try again tomorrow.'

'Yes,' Laura said, feeling relieved. He was obviously not anxious about her absence at the moment. 'It will be better tomorrow. If it is, with a bit of luck, I'll be home.' She crossed her fingers superstitiously and breathed a silent prayer of entreaty.

Mike tried Paris again later, but without success.

'It will be too late for him to start for home now, anyway,' he reasoned.

He cooked the evening meal of steak and salad, and they ate it before a cosy fire. Laura kept a discreet distance, which he seemed quite happy to observe, and she began to feel more relaxed.

'Did Charlotte and Gervaise go to Paris on holiday?' she asked conversationally.

He shook his head. 'No. On business. My company has connections there, and Gervaise went to complete negotiations on a deal, and Charlotte has a boutique in Paris which she visits pretty frequently, though her base is her London boutique.'

'They sound very busy,' Laura commented. 'And they certainly have a lovely home.'

'Hmm,' he nodded. 'Not that they see much of it. As you say, they're always rushing off somewhere or another.'

His words had an odd sound, and Laura looked at him curiously. 'Don't you approve? I'd have thought you would have applauded their initiative.'

He nodded. 'I do. And, of course, it's their life.' His gaze went pensively to the fire and the leaping flames. 'Perhaps I'm beginning to think there might be more to life than just success in business.'

Laura was tempted to ask him to expand, but some sixth sense warned her she might find herself on dangerous ground. She steered the conversation around to the subject of Gladstone House, outlining some of her ideas for the various rooms—a subject that kept both of them absorbed for the rest of the evening.

Later, in the pretty guest room, Laura sat on the edge of the bed, listening to the howl of the wind and the gusty beat of the rain against the window panes, and thought about the comfortable evening she'd just passed, and which she hadn't believed could be possible.

Perhaps this had been his real reason for getting her away from the hotel: to lull her into a false sense of security in this cosy setting. She was vaguely puzzled by the fact that Mike hadn't attempted to take advantage of the situation. She'd half expected him to make a pass at her, but, apart from the occasional intensity of his gaze as he'd looked at her, he'd maintained the distance she'd tried to put between them. And perhaps that was part of his plan too, she reasoned a little confusedly: to undermine her wary defences and take her by surprise.

So much for her plans to keep Mike Brady out of her life! she thought ironically. That had been her intention, and yet here she was, forced to live practically in his pocket, with no immediate way of escape.

The thoughts went around in her brain, taking her nowhere.

The best thing she could do, in the circumstances, was sleep until morning, when maybe the storm would have exhausted itself sufficiently for Gervaise to come with the helicopter. But, as she lay in the clean, scented bed, her treacherous mind reminded her that Mike Brady was in the next room. Her even more treacherous senses kept reliving the feelings she'd experienced in his arms that morning.

At last, unable to bear her churning restlessness, she put on the bedside light and sat up to read a magazine which was on the bedside table. She turned the glossy pages, trying to concentrate on what should have been an interesting article.

Thunder rumbled in the distance, and Laura jumped as a bright flash of lightning stabbed unexpectedly deeply into her room. The bedside lamp flickered and then, as lightning flashed again, went out, plunging the room into sudden darkness.

Laura gasped. Stay calm, my girl, she warned herself. It will come back on in a minute.

But it didn't, and, as two more brilliant flashes cut through the gloom, Laura couldn't help a little cry of alarm.

When Mike Brady had asked her if she was afraid of storms, she'd denied it, and thought she was telling the truth. But now, after seeing huge trees uprooted and flung down like matchsticks in the raging wind, this further evidence of elemental violence had her mouth dry and her heart beating unsteadily.

Maybe she should go downstairs to find out what had happened to the light. Anything was better than sitting here, alone in the dark, wondering. She got out of bed and was crossing the darkened room when a knock sounded and the door opened. Mike stood there, dimly silhouetted, and carrying a torch.

'Are you all right?' He flicked the beam up to inspect her face.

'I'm fine.' Laura brought her arm up to protect her eyes from the dazzle. 'And that's the truth, so there's no need for the third degree.'

Mike chuckled, a deep, rich sound that eased her tension. 'I'm glad to see you still have your sense of humour.'

Laura moved gingerly towards him, silently admitting that the warm strength of his hand, as he took hers, was a comfort. 'What happened? Has a fuse blown?'

'No. A little more serious than that, I think. It looks as if the storm has damaged the electricity cables somewhere. Perhaps some more falling trees. The phone's gone off, too.'

Laura groaned. 'Oh, wonderful! Now we really are marooned.'

He drew her towards him. 'Come on downstairs. Perhaps we can make a cup of hot chocolate, or something. Fortunately the stove is gas and it's still in working order.'

Candles were already lit on the kitchen table, and Laura sat down while Mike put a saucepan of milk on the stove. When it boiled he stirred it into the chocolate in the mugs and brought them to the table.

'This is really quite romantic, isn't it?' he said, with a mischievous grin that made Laura grimace. He really was piling on the charm, she noted sourly. She would have to be careful.

'I'm afraid I'm not in the mood for romance,' she replied quellingly. 'I'm just wondering if I'll ever get home.'

He watched her openly in the flickering light of the candles, which darkened his blue eyes and cast dancing shadows there.

'"Home is where the heart is", Laura. And I wonder where that is?'

The silly cliché made her angry. 'Not with you,' she hit back sharply. 'No matter how much you may try to——' She stopped abruptly, biting back the rest of the sentence. She'd been about to say, 'No matter how much you may try to convince me it might be possible.' It was all a sham, the product of his wish for revenge. What a fool she'd be to be taken in by the promise of his lips . . . the guile in his yes.

Pinned by his gaze, Laura blinked nervously and, at this evidence of her disquiet, his lips curved in a slow, sensuous smile which seemed to melt her bones. She had difficulty repressing a shiver.

'Are you cold?' He reached across and touched her hand.

'No.' Laura drew it away hastily.

'Why are you so nervous when I touch you, Laura? What is it you're afraid of?'

'I'm sure you'd like me to say it was you,' she hissed furiously. 'But if I did I'd be lying.'

She knew she was lying when she said it wasn't him, but he would never know that. She stood up. 'There's no point in this conversation, or in staying up any longer. I'm going back to bed.'

He shook his head and leaned back in the chair. 'Happy dreams, Laura,' he said mockingly as she walked away—and then, as she reached the doorway, 'Do you want a candle?'

She shook her head, afraid to stop or speak in case he saw her trembling.

The staircase was lighted dimly by the tall window, but the corridor leading to her room was almost pitch black, and she half wished she'd accepted his offer of a candle. She needed to use the bathroom, and it was more by luck than good judgement that she found it.

As she was about to leave, she heard Mike coming up the stairs, and was tempted to come out and let him light her way to her room, but pride kept her stubbornly still.

When all was silent, she risked stepping out of the bathroom. Her eyes were slowly growing accustomed to the dimness, and in a little while she found her way to her bedroom door, sighing with relief as she stepped inside. The room was dark, but the light counterpane glowed faintly, guiding her towards the bed. She'd pulled back the covers, and was getting into bed, before she realised her mistake.

Mike's arms came out to hold her, drawing her tight against him.

'My little darling!' His voice was husky with disbelief, and sent shafts of heat spearing through Laura's body. 'I didn't dare hope you would come.'

'Mike! Oh, please!' she cried in a panicky voice. 'This wasn't intentional. I got lost!'

'Fate...or Freudian slip?' he queried softly, his lips beginning to tantalise her ear. 'Whatever, you're where you belong—in my arms.'

'That's not true,' she denied in a cracked voice, as shivers ran the length of her spine.

'Isn't it?'

He cupped her chin with one hand, bringing her mouth to his possessively, and she gasped as she felt the tension of his lean, naked body against hers through the thin silk of her borrowed nightgown. His lips moved on hers with a hungry need that stirred in her an almost instant response, which she struggled to repress. She couldn't give in now. It would be a betrayal of herself—and more—a betrayal of Joe, who had already begun to hope...

Hardening her lips against his, Laura tried to fight the rising fire and groaned in despair as his tongue flicked sensuously against her soft lower lip before entering the warm moist recesses of her mouth.

This is madness! her mind screamed, but her body was melting, enveloped in a slow-burning fire as his hands began a possessive exploration of her body. He kissed her arching throat, and the touch of his mouth on her skin brought an unbearable longing that pulsated deep inside.

'Mike, please!' she murmured raggedly.

'Hush!' he chided softly, brushing his lips fleetingly against hers, before tracing a path of fire down towards her breasts, which were already swelling under his questing lips, the nipples erect and sensitised to the butterfly caress of his tongue.

'No!' She gave an agonised cry and struggled to make space between them. He brought his head up to look at her, his face shadowed, his brilliant blue eyes muted to soft grey in the dim light. 'This shouldn't be happening,' she muttered hopelessly. 'And we both know it.'

'I know nothing,' he said thickly, 'except that I want you.'

He slipped the nightgown deftly from her, and she seemed powerless to resist as he gathered her close again, setting her unbearably aflame. He kissed her fiercely, his lips and the lean length of his body holding her prisoner to a painful yearning that it was impossible to identify, but which she knew only he could satisfy.

'And you want me, Laura.' He lifted his mouth to whisper fiercely. 'What's happening now was always inevitable.'

He was right, one part of her knew, and it was the only comfort she could find as she surrendered to the sweet, irresistible persuasion of his lips as they descended once more on hers. But all thought of right or wrong, or even inevitability, disappeared on a wave of pure feeling as his kiss deepened, and his hands aroused her to that joyous peak, and he moved, at last, to fulfil her body with his in ecstatic union.

It seemed a lifetime before passion was spent, and he had entered her again, more than once, before they fell asleep, exhausted, in each other's arms.

And Laura's dreams were sweet. Throughout the night she dreamed his hands smoothed her silky skin, as lightly as butterflies' wings, and his arms held her with a gentle warmth. At some point, she felt herself lifted into space and deposited in a cool sea, which cradled her deeper into contented sleep.

She woke to a pale yellow light which flooded the guest room. For a moment she was disorientated, and lay still, letting the slow memories return, wondering if she'd dreamed the whole thing. But she was naked between the cool linen sheets and there was no sign of the silk nightgown she'd borrowed.

She groaned softly with the realisation that it had been no dream. She had surrendered herself to him and they had made love again and again in the long night. She put her hands to her suddenly hot cheeks as she remembered her eager responses, afraid to look inside for the reasons. What spell had he cast upon her? she asked fretfully. But innate honesty led her to admit that there was no magic she could blame for her behaviour, except the magic of the attraction that drew her irresistibly to him.

Did he know, she wondered miserably, how impossible it would be for her, after last night, to be content with any other man as her lover? Probably, she acknowledged despairingly. His love had been no gift of love or pleasure, but rather a punishment for her previously having rejected him.

And what further proof of that did she need, but that she was here, in her own bed, rather than waking up in his arms?

In the heat of his loving he had told her she belonged there, but the cold light of day denied it. He had done with her and then had carried her to her room so that she would know it was over.

He would get her home somehow and then leave her, his revenge complete.

CHAPTER NINE

MIKE was in the kitchen when Laura eventually went downstairs. He was standing at the stove frying bacon and eggs as she entered, and the aroma filled the air.

'Good morning.' He flashed her a brief look over his shoulder.

'Good morning,' she murmured in return, trying to read his mood in the posture of his body, and failing.

He was wearing a thin towelling robe, which outlined the broad shoulders and taut hips, and revealed the muscular legs and feet thrust into leather mules. Even first thing in the morning, with his hair a little tousled, he was stunning, and Laura had to look away as strange stirrings began inside her, feelings she would just as soon forget.

'Want some breakfast?'

Annoyed by the calmness of his voice when her own throat was restricted by the speed of her heartbeat, accelerated uncomfortably by the sight of him, Laura wanted to refuse, but the delicious smell of the food had made her suddenly hungry.

'Yes, please,' she said, a little unsteadily. 'Do you want me to help?'

'No, thanks. Just sit.'

Laura did as she was bidden, and he nodded his head in satisfaction at her obedience. She waited, trembling a little, for him to mention last night, but he seemed engrossed in his cooking.

'It's almost ready.' He heaped two eggs and several rashers of bacon on a plate, and brought them to her at the table.

'Oh, that's too much,' she protested. 'I don't normally eat cooked breakfast.'

He shook his head. 'I'd try if I were you. You may need it.'

'Thanks.' Laura looked up at him expectantly. 'Why? Is there something happening at last? The storm's obviously over. Are we able to make a move?'

He filled up his own plate before answering her, and came to sit down opposite. His feet touched hers beneath the table, and Laura was hard pressed not to show her reactive shudder. She sighed with relief as he applied himself to his food, seeming unaware of her minor crisis.

'Not yet,' he answered her question after tasting the food on his plate. 'The storm's over but the roads won't be cleared by any magic wand. We'll have to wait for Gervaise and the helicopter. It's the only way we can be sure of completing the journey home.'

Laura felt a sinking dismay. 'How long will it be before Gervaise arrives?'

He shrugged. 'Later this afternoon, at an optimistic guess—that's if he can make it at all.'

She groaned inwardly. A whole day and another night in his company would just about demolish her teetering defences. Seated across the table from him now, she was already feeling the strain of wanting to touch him and knowing it would be both foolish and fatal to do so.

There was a peculiar ache inside her, and she thought how strange it was that her hands, which last night had been free to explore him with a feverish need equal to his own, should now be forbidden to touch that body which had shown her such delight. The longing to reach across to him was almost overwhelming, but she fought it doggedly. Why add to his feelings of victory?

Was that what he was feeling this morning? she wondered futilely. Victory? She couldn't resist the urge to look at him, and she tried to read his face. His expression was annoyingly remote. Was it really disinterest, or iron self-control? Either way, it made him a dangerous companion, since she seemed quite capable of making a fool of herself all over again.

'Laura,' he began at last, and she looked up at him in surprise. 'I don't want you to think that last night——' He broke off as he saw the change in her expression to one of fury.

'Don't worry about last night,' she cut in. 'I understand.'

'Do you?' He made a sharp, exasperated sound. 'I wish I did.'

'Well, don't tax your brain.' She laughed shortly. 'It wasn't important.'

She watched his face harden with a grim satisfaction. If it was possible to rob him of some of his self-satisfaction, it would be worth the pain.

'Still playing the same old game, Laura,' he growled. 'Still trying to delude yourself.'

'I think you're the expert on delusions, Mike,' she retorted, sounding calm despite her inner trembling. 'Shall we dispense with the subject?'

He eyed her narrowly, probing deep into her shadowed eyes. 'OK. It seems there's nothing to be gained by prolonging it.'

'Nothing at all.'

She tried to concentrate on the food before her, but it was almost impossible to force it beyond the lump that had inexplicably risen in her throat. She groaned again, this time aloud, and he looked up.

'Does it bother you that much? Having to stay here for another day or so?'

Laura flushed under his discerning gaze, and avoided giving an answer by asking him a direct question.

'Are the phone lines still down?'

He nodded. 'As far as I know. At least, this line's still dead.'

'I was hoping to speak to Joe.'

His face softened a little. 'With a bit of luck you still might see him today.' He stood up. 'But it won't be until later on, and it might be better if you didn't hang around here fretting.'

'Have you got something in mind?'

'Yes. I thought we'd fill in time while we're waiting for Gervaise to turn up by taking a ride over to Gladstone House. I'd like to see if there's any storm damage.'

Laura coloured faintly. She hadn't given his house a thought. His concern reminded her that he was still her client, buying her time.

'Well, of course you must be anxious,' she conceded. 'But do you think we'll make it there?'

He shrugged his broad shoulders. 'It's only just the other side of the village, so we should manage it.'

'When do you want to start?' she asked.

'There's no time like the present.' He pushed his plate away with his food half eaten. 'Let me know when you're ready.'

Laura noted his lack of appetite with some satisfaction. He wasn't, after all, as cool, calm and collected as he wanted her to believe. Was his conscience bothering him? she wondered. Always supposing he had one, that was.

The morning was warm and sunny, the sky a complete contrast to the previous day. Laura's spirits lifted a little. Perhaps she'd get home today after all.

She wondered if storm damage was the only thing on Mike's mind. Perhaps, she thought uneasily, one taste of her surrender wasn't enough to repair his pride. If he was planning on taking her to the house to seduce her yet again, she thought a little maliciously, then he might have chosen an easier day and venue for it.

But it appeared from his solemn, withdrawn face that seduction was low on his list of present priorities. He didn't speak, except to warn her of potential pitfalls, until they had crested a rise and were looking down into a shallow valley, where the roof and chimney-pots of Gladstone House rose above the trees to the left of the river.

'Do you think there'll be any flooding?' Laura asked a little anxiously.

'The house is some distance from the river, and on higher ground,' he said, 'so it should have escaped flooding; but some of the trees close to the building might have to come down, if they haven't already.'

Laura realised, with guilty surprise, that she hadn't given a thought to either of those concerns, but it would certainly set back his plans if any serious damage had been done.

There was a man in the stable yard as they approached, and she heard Mike grunt with relief.

'Hello, Ted,' he called. 'I wondered if you'd be able to make it. Have you had a chance to check for damage yet?'

'From a quick look, everything seems OK,' Ted said as Mike dismounted and helped Laura down. 'But I dare say we'll find something amiss when we take a closer look.'

Laura trudged around behind them in her borrowed wellington boots, feeling a little extraneous. But Mike had been right; even this was better than hanging about the house all day fretting.

Their inspection showed a number of trees had come down at the old boundaries, and another, at the back of the house, had demolished a greenhouse and adjacent potting-shed. The roof of a disused scullery had lifted, and various slates were missing from sections of the main roof, but apart from that the house appeared to have escaped any serious damage.

'We've been lucky,' Mike said to Laura as they entered the house. 'Considering the age of Gladstone, it seems to be pretty solid, thank goodness.'

'Yes,' Laura agreed. It would certainly have made things difficult if any major interior problems had arisen. Not that it mattered quite so much now, since her own wedding wouldn't be taking place and Mike had yet to set any definite date for his.

Her time had become her own again, she realised, with the beginnings of relief. Her half-formed decision not to marry Hubert had, somewhere along the line, hardened into certainty. She'd progressed to a feeling of amazement that she ever could have contemplated anything so obviously wrong for her. It wouldn't be easy, telling Hubert and her mother that the wedding was off, but once that was done...

And the sudden clarity of her insight had nothing to do with what had happened between herself and Mike Brady these past two days. It wasn't that she was hoping something more meaningful might come of their relationship, she told herself firmly. Even she couldn't be that foolish.

But, following Mike through the beautifully proportioned rooms, Laura was aware of a painful feeling that it took her some time to recognise. She really loved this house and, once her job was done, she would have no further access to it. The sense of loss was almost as great as unrequited love. But then, how did she know? She had never loved and lost.

They were back again in the large square hall, and Mike gave a satisfied sigh.

'Now I know everything is all right, I think I could manage something to eat. How about lunch at the Inn?'

So, worry about Gladstone really had been the reason for his lack of appetite! Laura gave a silent laugh of self-mockery. Had she really been hoping for proof of a conscience?

However, the ride over had sharpened her own appetite, and lunch at the Inn was suddenly very appealing. She had nothing to lose and nothing, it seemed from Mike's distant attitude, to gain.

But later, as they sat over coffee—Laura's without whisky—she wondered if she'd been wrong.

'Laura,' he began suddenly, with a half-wary expression on his handsome face, 'I have a proposition to make, and I don't want you going off half cocked before I have a chance to put it to you properly.'

Laura eyed him uncertainly. 'I can't promise what my reaction is going to be to anything. But ask anyway.'

'Well.' His blue eyes settled on hers steadily. 'I have another job in mind for you when this one is complete, but it would be a long one and it would need a firm commitment from you.'

A faint stirring of excitement began in Laura. She hadn't known what to expect, but it hadn't been this.

'Go on,' she prompted guardedly. 'At least I can listen.'

He smiled at her. 'I think you'll like it, but your—er—prospective groom...might not find it so appealing, since you'd have to be away from home from time to time.'

'Let me worry about that,' Laura said, incautious in her excitement.

He paused, his eyes searching hers, as though for some hidden message, but he was fishing in vain.

Laura hid a smile. She wasn't going to tell him, but Hubert's views on her work weren't now going to be a problem. 'I wish you'd get to the point.'

'OK.' He seemed to release a pent-up breath. 'Here it is.' He settled back more comfortably into his chair. 'I went over to Paris last year with Gervaise, and we stayed overnight in a high-class little hotel, which made quite an impact on me at the time. The décor was getting a bit ropy, but the place had definite potential, given a little money being spent on it.' He stopped and raised his brows at her, as though to gauge her reaction. 'Interesting?'

'Possibly,' Laura nodded, trying to stifle the beginnings of elation. If this was what she thought it was...

He went on. 'I contacted the management earlier this year to see whether they'd be interested in refurbishing, using my stuff, but they weren't, because they were thinking of selling the place.'

A wide smile spread across his face, and Laura bit her lip to prevent an answering smile lighting up her own face. She wasn't absolutely sure what was coming next, but she couldn't resist taking a guess.

'You've bought it?'

'Right first time.'

He leaned towards her, and Laura found herself leaning in his direction too. But now another idea had popped into her mind, and she was almost too breathless to voice it.

'And... and you want me to... redesign the whole interior?' she said, her voice rising incredulously. 'Before you've even seen the results of my work with Gladstone House?'

He shook his head impatiently. 'I don't need that kind of proof. I know what you're capable of.'

She stared disbelievingly at him. 'You really trust me with something this big?'

He smiled into her wide, excited eyes. 'Why else would I be asking?'

Laura had to stifle an urge to hug him. 'Oh, Mike!' she breathed, her voice husky with emotion. 'You don't know how much that means to me.'

He gripped her hands in his. 'Then you'll do it?'

'But of course. I'd love to.'

It was just what she needed, at just the right time. A good long commission, with lots of designing work to absorb her attention, and time away from home for the dust of her cancelled wedding to settle. She might even be able to take Joe with her... give him a little holiday before he started school.

'How quickly do you want to start?' she asked.

He looked at her carefully. 'Fairly quickly. In fact, as soon as Gladstone's finished. The sooner the place is done up, the sooner it can be re-opened and a start made on recouping the money spent.'

Laura had been about to say that suited her well, when he asked, 'If you want the job, it could mean putting back the date of the wedding.'

Laura paused. 'Yours or... mine?'

'Possibly both,' he said, with a strange light in his blue eyes. 'The project can't really wait for weddings and honeymoons.'

The excitement drained slowly from Laura's face as an awful suspicion began to grow. Perhaps she'd underestimated the strength of his desire for revenge. Did it now entail wrecking her marriage to Hubert? And was he prepared to disappoint his own bride, by postponing his own wedding, in order to do it?

She frowned at him. 'Excuse me if I'm wrong, but I sense an underlying reason for your wonderful offer. Would I be right in thinking that what you'd really like is to prevent my wedding altogether?'

His eyes narrowed and his face was suddenly grim. 'If you want the truth, I don't think Hubert Laine is the right man for you.'

Laura took a sharp inward breath. 'And what makes you think it's any of your business?'

He replied, his voice tight and furious, 'You can ask me that... after last night?'

'"Last night"?' she repeated. 'What was last night, but evidence that I'm capable of lust? Does it shock you that women can feel it as strongly as men?'

She wanted to hurt him, and since his pride was all she could attack then that would be her target. She gave a bitter laugh. 'Your performance scored quite high marks, by the way.'

His grip on her hands became a vice, crushing the delicate bones until Laura cried out. People around them heard, and were beginning to take notice.

'Let's get out of here,' he hissed.

Without waiting for her answer, he hailed the waiter for the bill and threw the money on to the table without even counting it. Grabbing Laura's wrist, he all but dragged her out of the Inn. He retained his grip as he took her round the back to the stable, where the horses had been left.

It was empty except for their two horses, munching contentedly on a couple of forkfuls of hay, and he pulled her into a shadowed corner.

'So last night was simply lust, was it?' he gritted without preamble. 'And what does that make you? A prospective bride who can go to bed with any man who takes her fancy? It doesn't say much for you, does it?' His eyes were like shards of bright blue ice.

Laura glared back at him defiantly. 'No more than it says for you, I suppose. Or is that different?'

'You tell me,' he countered grimly. 'Or, better still, ask Hubert Laine how it feels.'

'And what precisely do you mean by that?' There was a feeling at the back of Laura's mind that made her oddly uncomfortable, but it was swamped by her anger.

'Think about it,' he snapped, and she had never seen him so cold.

Laura glared at him, hating him for the way he brought everything down to his own level. Up until this moment she had felt no guilt. What had happened between them had seemed so natural and right at the time that there had been no thought of shame, or even Hubert's rights as her intended husband. In fact, she'd given him no thought at all. It came as a shock that had her shuddering. Was she really that selfish? Perhaps she was doing him a favour by releasing him from his commitment to her.

'Hubert's not a man like that——' she cried, her voice shaking with repressed fury. She stopped as she saw Mike's cynical smile. Oh, why was she even attempting to justify anything to a man like him?

'Do you mean he's sexless?' Mike goaded. 'Is that why you needed me? To relieve your frustrations?' He laughed harshly. 'Maybe you should talk to one another. You might find you're both playing the same game.'

The old feeling of revulsion swept over her; just to mention Hubert in the same breath as——

'Leave him out of this!' She beat against his chest in sudden fury. 'This is between you and me.'

'Is it?' He pulled her suddenly into his arms and kissed her in fierce punishment, only lifting his head when she was on the verge of suffocation. 'Was that lust enough for you?' he growled. 'Or do you fancy a roll in the hay?'

'Why you——!' It was impossible to speak her feelings. With the remnants of her strength, Laura pushed him away and her hand flew out to hit against his cheek with more force than she knew she was capable of.

In a reflex action, she cowered away from him, appalled by the deep red marks of the blow against his cheek, and half expecting him to retaliate. But, as she backed a little fearfully into the corner, the tension of anger suddenly went out of him.

He shrugged. And his shrug said it all. There was nothing left between them now—not even anger.

Everything was spoiled, she thought despondently as he brought the horses out and helped her mount. She couldn't even begin to pretend a professional attitude, she realised numbly as they rode back in silence. If he wanted her to finish Gladstone House she would do it, because she couldn't bear to abandon a project which had become so close to her heart; but after that was finished...

Surprisingly, she was able to feel regret for the lost opportunity of the hotel in Paris. Had it been real, she wondered, or just something he'd thought up to get her to postpone or even cancel her wedding? What had he intended to do if she had? she wondered with a strange sense of detachment. Go on making love to her until she was hopelessly besotted and then drop her? Would that make them even?

She looked at his absorbed profile as he rode alongside her. He seemed oblivious now to everything except the task of getting them back to Charlotte's house, so she was free to study him without him being aware, and her treacherous heart began its familiar painful tattoo against her ribs.

If that had been his plan, she mused sadly, then it undoubtedly would have succeeded. She was already more than a little in love with him. Despite everything she now knew about him, the contempt she felt for his perverted motives, she still wanted him.

'Do you think Gervaise will be back yet?' she asked, to break the painful silence.

He turned his head to look at her a little dazedly, almost as though he'd forgotten her very existence.

'I don't know,' he shrugged. 'It's possible.'

Oh, please, God, she prayed fervently. Let him be there. I couldn't bear another night... in the same house... remembering...

'He's arrived. There's the helicopter,' Mike said as they reached the crest of the hill, and he sounded almost as relieved as she was. Now she'd uncovered his motives, he was probably as anxious to get rid of her as she was to go, she thought grimly.

With a bit of luck, she would be home again soon. Not that that would be any haven, she thought with sudden bitterness. Apart from the relief of seeing Joe, the time ahead was destined to be even more fraught than the last few hours, but she was determined to see things through to the only proper conclusion. She would see Hubert as soon as she possibly could, and would tell him she couldn't marry him.

CHAPTER TEN

THERE was a man in the kitchen, finishing off a meal, as Mike entered, followed by a subdued Laura.

A beautiful blonde woman came out of the pantry with a plate of cheeses, and almost dropped it as she caught sight of Mike.

'Mike!' she squealed. 'So it was you!' She hugged him delightedly. 'We thought we had squatters.'

'You did,' he grimaced. 'But now you're back we'll be leaving.'

Charlotte had obviously been highly pleased to see her brother, but her smile faded as she caught sight of Mike's expression. 'Something wrong?'

'Nothing that matters,' he said shortly as he sat down at the table opposite Gervaise.

Laura, standing a little hesitantly behind him, felt a flare of temper. That little dart was intended for her skin, she knew, and he couldn't have said more plainly how he felt about their quarrel. It had mattered 'nothing'.

Charlotte grimaced over his head and rolled her eyes at Laura, in a silent question. Laura shrugged, in no mood for satisfying the woman's curiosity. No doubt Mike would tell her, soon enough, anything he wanted her to know.

'Do you want to eat?' Charlotte was obviously not offended by Laura's refusal to communicate, and Laura thought she seemed a much nicer person than her spoiled brother. In different circumstances, they might possibly have become very good friends.

'No, thanks,' Mike said. 'We had lunch at the Inn. But I wouldn't mind a cup of coffee.' He flashed Laura a quick glance. 'I think Ms Maxwell prefers tea.'

'Not always,' Laura corrected him stubbornly, and turned to Charlotte. 'I'd love a cup of coffee, thanks.'

Mike sat down, and waved a hand for Laura to sit. Swallowing her resentment at his imperiousness, she sat beside him. The ball was in his court at the moment, and there wasn't much she could do about it.

'Aren't you going to introduce the young lady?' Gervaise's eyes twinkled at Laura.

'Gervaise Deschamps——' Mike inclined his head towards his brother-in-law '—this is Laura Maxwell, the interior designer who's doing up Gladstone House for me.' The introduction was made in a businesslike way that made it possible for Laura to assume some poise.

'I'm pleased to meet you,' she said, extending her hand.

'*Charmed* to meet you!' Gervaise stood up to kiss her outstretched fingers with a continental flourish, and she wondered why, with a name like Gervaise, she hadn't guessed he was French.

'I've been telling Laura about the plans for La Grande,' Mike went on. 'And I've offered her the job of re-designing the interior, if she wants it.'

Caught off guard, Laura started. So the job was real after all. A shaft of renewed excitement sped through her, but she swiftly doused it. There was no way she could even think of prolonging her association with Mike Brady—not even for a marvellous job such as the one he was offering her.

Mike turned and caught her in his sardonic gaze, obviously enjoying her discomfiture, which was evident in the flush which rose to her cheeks.

'And are you going to take it?' Gervaise asked her with a smile.

She felt like saying, 'Never in a million years!' but there was something in her not yet ready to burn her boats entirely.

'I—I'm . . . thinking about it,' she supplied at last.

Mike snorted. 'Well, at least that's more information than I've managed to elicit from Ms Maxwell,' he said grimly.

Charlotte came with their coffee, and Mike stood up. 'I think I'll take mine to the sitting-room.' He shot a commanding look at Gervaise. 'Come and tell me what happened in Paris.'

'Have you two quarrelled?' Charlotte asked bluntly as the men went into the sitting-room with their coffee.

Laura sighed. 'We've had a disagreement, yes.'

Charlotte's face lit up. 'A lovers' quarrel?'

Laura flushed. 'Your brother is my client, nothing more,' she lied, taking the precaution of crossing her fingers. 'And we're having a little difficulty, at the moment, in seeing eye to eye.'

Charlotte nodded. 'Want to talk about it?'

'Not really,' Laura said, though she dearly would have loved to unburden herself to someone.

'It might help,' Charlotte encouraged. 'I know my brother better than most. I ought to; we've been orphans together since our teens. I can't claim to know what makes him tick exactly, but I can tell he's interested in you.'

Laura gave a sigh. 'He's interested, but for all the wrong reasons.' She shook her head. 'It's a long story.'

'But intriguing, I hope.' Charlotte poured two cups of coffee from the percolator, and sat down at the table she'd just cleared of dishes. 'I've got all the time in the world, and I love a good story.'

'It's not a *good* story,' Laura told her as she sat down opposite and gazed pointedly into her coffee-cup. 'And I don't really think I should talk about it.'

Charlotte patted her hand. 'Fair enough. I understand.'

Laura doubted if she did. There were so many things she didn't understand herself.

Mike came back into the kitchen. 'I'm ready to get back to town now, if you are.' He addressed himself coolly to Laura. He had an air of impatience about him, and it seemed that he was as anxious to get rid of Laura now as Laura was to be gone.

She stood up. 'I'm more than ready,' she told him grimly.

A little later, she was standing alongside the helicopter while he started up the engine. Charlotte came out of the house with a fleece-lined jacket, which she offered to Laura for the flight. 'You'll need this. It's chilly once you're up in the air.'

'But it won't be for long, surely?' Laura protested. 'We're hardly that far away from home by helicopter. And, besides, you may need it.'

'You can bring it back when the roads are clear,' Charlotte reassured her, her eyes meeting Laura's with a clear look that said more than her words. 'Or I could pick it up myself. We could have lunch. I'm in town every day when things are normal.'

Laura's eyes went to Mike's face to see what he felt about this implication of a continuing acquaintance with his sister. He was frowning, but said nothing.

'I . . . I'd rather not,' she said hesitantly.

'Oh, put the damned thing on!' Mike ordered in sudden irritation. 'I can always return it myself, or you can leave it behind in the helicopter when you've finished with it and Gervaise will bring it back.'

Charlotte shot him a hard look. 'Trust a man to find a simple solution.'

Mike's eyes met hers briefly, and he gave a harsh little laugh. 'Stop interfering, Charlie,' he said tersely.

Laura had no time to ponder that remark as she was thrust into the helicopter and told to strap herself in. With a last wave, Charlotte stood back, well out of range of the blades, her blonde hair blowing about wildly in the air blast as the machine began to lift.

Waving from the window, Laura wondered if they really would meet again as friends, independent of Mike Brady.

Florence's garden was large enough to land the helicopter, and Laura saw Joe come spilling out of the house even before they'd landed. He came rushing down the garden, with Laura's parents in his wake.

Mike cut the engine and got out to help Laura down.

'This is brilliant, Mike!' Joe cried, his eyes like stars. 'Are we going for a ride now?'

Laura felt a stab of dismayed anger as Mike lifted the little boy up into his arms. Surely he could see it would be better for Joe's sake to keep him at arm's length, rather than encourage this hero worship?

'Calm down, young Joe,' he said with a grin. 'There's a time and a place for everything, and this isn't it.'

'Oh.' Joe's face fell in disappointment. 'But I want——'

'We all want,' Mike cut in firmly. 'Sometimes we get . . . and sometimes we don't.' He put the boy on his feet and ruffled his hair. 'You must learn to be patient.'

Undaunted, Joe persisted. 'If I wait until next week, will you take me then?'

Mike tweaked his nose. 'Perhaps.' His brilliant blue eyes met Laura's for a brief instant over Joe's head, seeming to relay a message, which she was too annoyed to bother interpreting.

'The answer to that question is no,' she said in a furious whisper, as her mother drew nearer. 'Whatever you're up to now, Mike Brady, you can leave Joe out of it.'

He held her gaze narrowly. 'And what if I can't?' he replied softly, and it sounded like a threat.

Laura didn't resist when her mother insisted she stay the night. For the moment, she was reluctant to be alone with her thoughts.

The sight of her wedding dress, carefully shrouded in polythene, and hanging outside of the wardrobe in her room, gave her even less pleasure than usual. It reminded her of what she must do, and it wasn't a task she much relished.

Wallowing in the bath, she thought about telling her mother right away of her decision not to marry

Hubert, and get the worst over, but decided it wouldn't be right to tell Florence before she had spoken to Hubert. She went down to dinner a little early, to give herself the opportunity of ringing him to ask him to meet her, but there was no reply.

Over dinner, Laura answered Florence's inevitable questions with care, on the premise of least said soonest mended, giving only the sketchiest of details. She saw her mother's mouth open and then close in silence. From her expression, that was far from all she wanted to hear, and hastily Laura changed the subject.

'Have you . . . seen anything of Hubert?' she asked tentatively, starting her own ball rolling. 'I hope you told him there was nothing to worry about?'

'No.' Laura saw, with mild astonishment, the flush staining her mother's cheeks, as she continued stiffly, 'We haven't been able to tell him anything. Hubert was out of town too. Apparently, he got cut off by the same storm.'

'Really?' Laura's brows rose. So that explained the lack of reply on the telephone. She was surprised although, thinking about it, it wasn't really that surprising. The unexpectedly violent storm must have stranded a great many people.

She smiled inwardly as she thought how it must have irritated Florence to be robbed of her ally in her time of crisis. Hubert had obviously been undergoing a similar crisis of his own, so there would be no need for explanations on either side. Except, she thought grimly, that, in her case, she'd been marooned with a man whom she had allowed, perhaps even encouraged, to make love to her.

Still, now she'd decided not to marry Hubert, she wouldn't be forced to choose between honesty or prevarication. At the moment, she felt totally incapable of either.

'Has he managed to get back yet?'

'Not to our knowledge,' Florence answered impatiently as though Hubert had somehow let her down. 'His housekeeper has a message for him to ring as soon as he arrives home.'

That should cheer him up, Laura thought ironically. The poor man had probably been in a frenzy for days, rehearsing his own explanations for a predicament he didn't know they shared.

But, the following day, Hubert still hadn't arrived home and, in the odd moments when she wasn't engaged on her designs for Gladstone House, Laura wondered if there was any cause to worry.

Viewing the situation practically, from her own experience, she realised that, depending on where he'd been at the time the storm broke, it might still be impossible to find roads open for travel. A lot of areas were still suffering the after-effects of the freak storm.

But at least the telephone service had been restored to most areas, and Laura had rung his house, more than once, leaving a message for him to contact her.

But it was two more days before she heard from him. He rang in the late afternoon, just as she was about to take a shower.

'Laura. I have to see you as soon as possible.' He sounded flustered and uncertain and not at all his usual restrained self.

'Well, of course.' Laura hid her astonishment at his peculiar tone. 'I've been trying to get hold of you for days. Are you all right? I hear you were cut off by the storm . . .'

'I was sure you would have heard.' He sounded oddly belligerent. 'But I think you might at least give me the opportunity to try to explain.'

'Well, I agree, of course,' she found herself saying reassuringly. 'As a matter of fact, I have something to say to you too——'

'Laura!' he broke in, sounding stricken. 'Don't say or do anything until I've had a chance to speak to you. I'll be there in about half an hour.'

She had a hasty shower instead of the relaxing one she had been looking forward to, and was further irritated when the telephone rang again, before she was even dry.

It was Mike Brady, which didn't improve her temper.

Since his departure in the helicopter, she'd tried to put him out of her mind. The fact that the designs she was working on were for him had been pushed to the back of her mind as she concentrated on colours and harmonies for the rooms she loved.

'Hello, Laura,' he said, in answer to her clipped greeting. 'How's it going?'

The deep, pleasant sound of his voice reverberated through her nervous system. 'With the designs, you mean?'

He gave a mirthless laugh. 'What else?'

There was no answer to that, she thought bitterly. 'A few more days and I'll be finished.'

'Really?' He sounded pleased, but concerned. 'You must have burned a lot of midnight oil.'

'Yes, I suppose I must have,' she admitted. But she wasn't going to admit that working until she was exhausted was what had kept her from thinking about him during the day and dreaming about him during the night. 'I wanted to get it finished and off my plate.'

'Well, fine!' He sounded a little edgy now, Laura noted with some satisfaction, as though her desire to have the thing over and done with had offended him.

'So! If that's all you want to know...' For some reason, she had begun to tremble, and it was suddenly imperative to finish this conversation before her shaky voice told him that he could still have a ridiculously disturbing effect on her.

'Not quite,' he said evenly. 'Since you're this far on, you really ought to get your orders in at Designers' Choice for delivery.'

She smiled wryly to herself. As though his deliveries wouldn't have first priority!

'I haven't neglected that aspect. It's all in hand. You brought some patterns for me, remember?'

'Yes,' he agreed. 'But a visit to the store is surely called for? Let me know when you want to come and I'll make certain I'm available.'

'There's no need for you to be there.' Laura tried to hide a surge of dismay. The last thing she wanted now was the disturbance of seeing him again. 'You did say, at the beginning, that I was to have a free hand,' she reminded him, 'and I already know what I want. It's only a question of matching my ideas to your current ranges and, to be frank, I'd rather browse alone.'

There was a pause before he said, 'We've got to meet some time, Laura . . . to finalise everything.'

'I know.' Laura swallowed an inexplicable lump in her throat. 'But I'm not ready for that yet.'

'Aren't you?' There seemed to be a wealth of meaning behind the words that set Laura's pulses racing.

'No. And, if you don't mind, I really must go. I have someone calling shortly.'

'Anyone I know?' His voice was suddenly hard.

'Perhaps,' she replied, with equal harshness.

He was quiet for some time until she thought he'd cut off. Then he said in a guarded voice, 'Have you seen Laine yet?'

Laura frowned. 'Why do you ask?'

'I just wondered if you'd . . . sorted things out.'

Anger rose in her as she remembered the conversation in the barn, and it was obvious he was still trying to influence her in the matter of her marriage. She was almost tempted to go on with it just to show him he couldn't interfere with her life, but she wasn't that much of a fool.

'I don't know why you should be so interested,' she replied furiously. 'Because it's none of your damned business!'

She slammed down the receiver just as the doorbell rang. Hubert had obviously arrived, and the last thing she wanted was to meet him draped in nothing but a bath towel. She rushed into the bedroom to grab her robe before answering the door.

'Come in,' she invited, flustered by the residue of her anger. 'I'm sorry I'm not ready. I was delayed by a telephone call.' She waved him past. 'Go into the living-room and get yourself a drink, if you want one. I won't keep you long.'

She left him and went into the bedroom to dress quickly and apply a little make-up. Somehow, she needed that bit of camouflage to boost her courage. Her hand was shaking as she hastily brushed her hair. Mike Brady's call had thoroughly upset her, and she cursed him for it. She'd wanted to be calm and rational for this meeting with Hubert, not wound up and irritable.

She wasn't looking forward to what she had to do, but was sure that, once he'd had time to reflect on it, Hubert would realise that it was best for both of them. Nevertheless, the next few moments were bound to be very upsetting.

He was standing at the window, staring out into the small yard with its stoneware pots of flowers, its only concession to the name 'garden', studying the dull red wall of the building which overlooked it.

He turned, as she entered, and she noticed that he was very pale. He hadn't poured himself a drink.

'Do you want coffee?' she asked, and when he shook his head she felt relieved that she didn't have to waste time on making it. If she put this off much longer... 'Hubert,' she began, but he put up his hand.

'Laura, please! I know what you're going to say, and I don't blame you. There is no justification I can offer except to say that I'm a man, with the same weaknesses as others, but——' He broke off, his face suffused with red.

'What kind of weaknesses?' Laura stared at him in puzzlement. 'I don't understand.'

'You don't?' He looked shaken. 'Do you mean that Brady didn't tell you?'

She frowned, her mind trying to piece together some apparent but elusive pattern. 'Tell me what?'

Hubert sucked in his cheeks in a gesture that was almost comical. 'Oh, lord! I assumed...'

'Hubert,' she began, with restrained impatience, and then stopped as she suddenly remembered the voice in the corridor at the hotel which she hadn't quite been able to place.

Silently, she thought about what had happened after the trees had fallen, startling them both. People had rushed out into the corridor, and Mike had gone too. A woman had been yelling and a man had spoken about his wife in a harassed voice, vaguely familiar, but she hadn't quite been able to recognise it. Mike had been standing in the doorway, blocking her view, holding her back. And now she knew why. He'd seen Hubert, and had wanted to protect her from seeing him herself. No wonder he had almost confined her to their room!

At least he'd cared enough for that. If he'd wanted to hurt her, to make sure her intended marriage didn't go ahead, he would have done his best to make sure she and Hubert *did* meet.

Laura could only guess at Mike's motives for keeping quiet about what he'd seen, but the fact remained that he hadn't told her. He'd given her the opportunity to make up her own mind. He'd also given Hubert the chance to make a clean breast of things—or not, as he chose—none of which seemed to be the behaviour of a vindictive man.

Had she been wrong all along in attributing his actions to a desire for revenge? But whichever way she tried to rationalise what had happened between them, Mike was still a man who had no qualms about making love to one woman while he was on the brink of marrying another. It was all so inconsistent. It just didn't make sense.

Hubert gave a funny little gasp, as though he'd been holding his breath for too long, startling Laura back to the present. She'd been quiet a long time, and had obviously been keeping the poor man on tenterhooks.

'Laura,' he began, taking a deep breath as though just about to jump in at the deep end. He was obviously going to make his confession, and she couldn't let him do it. Not without confessing herself in turn. All so unnecessary, since they would come out even. No. It was better that they should each keep their secrets and spare their own and each other's pride.

'Hubert,' she cut in quickly, 'before you go on, I'm afraid I have something to tell you. I've given it a lot of thought, and I've decided I can't marry you. I'm sorry.'

'But Laura,' he began, full of dismay, 'it doesn't have to be this way...'

'Please!' Laura leaned forward and kissed his cheek. 'It's the only way it can be, believe me. It wouldn't have worked... for either of us.'

CHAPTER ELEVEN

'HELLO, Laura! Remember me?' It took Laura some seconds to recognise the light, melodic voice.

'Charlotte!' Laura laughed. 'Who could forget you?'

'Who, indeed?' Charlotte returned sceptically, and went on before Laura could answer. 'I was wondering whether you'd like to get together with me for lunch? You could bring my jacket along with you.'

'Your jacket?' Laura bit her lip. 'Oh, lord! You know, I'd completely forgotten I still had it! I'm sorry. Have you been in need of it?'

'Of course I haven't. I've got a shop full of jackets just like it!' She chuckled. 'A bit of an exaggeration, but still. No, don't worry. I just mentioned it as a little gentle blackmail to oblige you to accept my invitation.'

'All quite unnecessary,' Laura assured her seriously. 'I'd love to see you again. Where do you want us to meet?'

'Do you know Caesar's?'

'Yes, I do. I go there quite often.' Laura paused as she remembered that Caesar's was just along the road from Designers' Choice. 'Charlotte,' she said tentatively, 'Mike isn't going to be there or anything, is he?'

'Of course not! Whatever gave you that idea?'

Laura felt foolish. 'I don't know. I suppose it's because Caesar's is close by his office. I thought maybe you might have invited him along as well, since we'd be in the vicinity.'

'Ahh!' The exclamation was a long one. 'And you wouldn't have liked that?'

Laura squirmed. 'I'm not saying I would have minded. I just wanted to be prepared in advance.'

'I see,' Charlotte said, causing Laura to wonder just what exactly she did see. 'But we won't be seeing him for lunch, unless by the most amazing coincidence. He's in Paris at the moment with Gervaise.'

'Oh! That's nice!' Laura was relieved, but aware of an empty feeling that had nothing to do with hunger. 'I mean, that they're such good friends,' she added.

'Hmm!' Charlotte murmured ironically. 'Sometimes I wonder. Especially when they gang up on me. Those two are as thick as thieves and twice as tricky.'

Laura laughed. She was grateful for the light touch. If anyone could cheer her up and lift her out of her feeling of anticlimax, it was Charlotte. 'What time will you be at Caesar's?' she asked.

'Twelve-thirty. Will that suit you?'

'Twelve-thirty will be fine.'

'And if you're not too busy for the rest of the afternoon, I thought I might show you my little empire. In my boutique, woman rules supreme.'

'Well, I...' Laura was about to plead pressure of work, which would have been no lie, but the temptation to play truant and satisfy her womanly curiosity was suddenly overwhelming. 'I am busy, actually, but I can catch up later. I'd love to come.'

'Good,' Charlotte said, sounding satisfied. 'See you at twelve-thirty, then.'

After Charlotte rang off, Laura moved restlessly from one thing to another, finding it impossible to get down to anything useful. If Charlotte had been anyone else but Mike's sister, it might have been different, but a lunchtime meeting with her was bound to bring her thoughts around to him.

Thinking about their last conversation on the telephone, she tried to remember what he'd actually said. It was obvious now that part of his purpose in ringing had been to find out, by some subtle means, whether Hubert had confessed to his clandestine affair, and, if so, what her reaction had been.

She supposed it was a point in Mike's favour that he hadn't told her what he'd seen that night. If he'd been really intent on breaking up her forthcoming wedding, he might have used the situation to his advantage. The outcome of her knowing wouldn't have been entirely predictable, of course, especially in view of her own similar situation, but it could be guaranteed to create a disturbance of some sort in her relationship.

She remembered his cryptic remark, made in anger, advising her to ask Hubert's opinion on cheating, which she hadn't at the time understood, but which was now obvious. When the news of her cancelled wedding reached him, as it was bound to do shortly, he would probably think he'd had something to do with her decision, but she couldn't help that, and she would be neither confirming nor denying his assumptions.

She decided that if Charlotte asked about the wedding she wouldn't lie, but she wouldn't bring up the subject herself. There was no doubt in her mind that she'd made the right decision about Hubert, but somehow her pride had become involved, and she didn't want to put any feathers in Mike Brady's cap.

She wondered if he'd yet made any firm commitment to his own wedding day, and felt depressed by her attempts to tell herself it didn't matter.

Charlotte was sitting in a corner, fairly close to the door, and waved an airy hand as Laura entered.

'Sorry I'm a little late,' Laura said, kissing the blonde woman's raised cheek. 'I had a job finding a parking space.'

Charlotte grimaced. 'I could have picked you up if I'd thought. It would have saved the bother of parking and running around in two separate cars.'

'And then you'd have had the bother of driving me home again!' Laura laughed.

'Well, I hope you won't want to go home too soon; as I said, I was planning on showing you around my boutique.'

Laura hadn't really escaped the subject of weddings. It came up again later when Charlotte was showing her over her boutique and they'd progressed to the bridal section.

'You have a really beautiful selection, Charlotte,' she commented, made breathless and somehow a little sad by the wonderful display.

'Yes. They are lovely, aren't they?' Charlotte agreed. 'But if you want to see a real knock-out, just look at this.' With the air of a town dignitary unveiling a work of art or a new building plaque, Charlotte swept back the curtain of a corner booth. 'Tell me what you think of that.'

An elegant sweep of her hand indicated the gown hanging there, and she smiled as it brought an awed gasp from Laura. 'It's just come in this morning, and I haven't had time to put it out on display. Isn't it gorgeous?'

It was more than gorgeous, Laura decided. But then, any description of the dress would fall far short of conveying its beauty, which was in the deceptively simple lines and exquisite cut of the lush cream satin, which somehow managed to combine sophistication with virginal understatement that was worlds away from the creation Florence had demanded from Mrs Brinson.

'It's absolutely stunning.'

'Mmm,' Charlotte murmured dreamily. 'Doesn't it make you wish you could have your Big Day all over again?' But the look of consternation on Laura's face wiped Charlotte's smile away. 'Oh, heavens!' she exclaimed contritely. 'Have I said something stupid?'

'Not really,' Laura said a little unevenly and then, because Charlotte looked so crestfallen, she added, 'Actually, I was going to get married again quite soon but I've cancelled the wedding.'

'Oh, my dear!' Charlotte's sympathetic arm came around Laura's shoulder. 'I'm so sorry.'

'Don't be,' Laura told her levelly. 'It would never have worked. I'm surprised I ever thought it could.'

Charlotte looked closely into her face before she said, with a tentative smile, 'Well, if you're that sure, it's more a cause for celebration than stricken looks.' She kissed Laura's cheek. 'Cheer up! Mr Right's just around the corner waiting for you, I'm sure of it.'

'I'm not!' Laura laughed wryly. 'As a matter of fact, I'm seriously considering combining the two careers of interior designing and being a nun——'

'What a waste that would be,' Mike Brady's deep, pleasant voice cut in, and Laura spun around, startled, to find him smiling cynically at her from the doorway. She glared at him, and then shot a look of angry consternation at Charlotte.

'Don't look at me like that, Laura,' she said. 'I didn't set this up, I swear.' To Mike she remarked irritably, 'You're supposed to be in Paris!'

Mike uncoiled himself from his relaxed stance against the door-jamb and came towards them, his mouth curled cynically. 'I have been in Paris; now I'm not. I didn't know I needed permission to return home early. I'll try to give you more warning next time.'

Charlotte snorted. 'Your brand of sarcasm never was the highest form of wit.' But she gave him a smile as he leaned to kiss her cheek. 'Where's Gervaise?'

'At the house. He asked me to tell you he's ravenous for a meal and a good woman, not necessarily in that order.'

She laughed. 'Well, he'll just have to wait. Laura and I haven't finished browsing.' She shot Laura an appeasing look.

Laura, who was still struggling with her emotions—a mixture of shock and fury—found it difficult to give her the reassurance she was looking for.

'Don't let me keep you,' she said tightly. 'I have to be getting back home now anyway.'

'Oh, don't rush off on my account.' Mike came and stood by Laura, his brows lifted quizzically. 'So, the wedding is off?'

She shot him a murderous glance. 'Yes. It is. Not that it's any of your business, Mr Eavesdropper Brady.'

'You weren't exactly whispering,' he returned with irritating calm, 'though I suppose I could have worn a bell around my neck.'

'I think a noose would be more appropriate!' Laura's eyes spat fire at him.

He put his hands suddenly on her shoulders in an ungentle grip which, nevertheless, sent shocks of excitement through her tense body. 'Disappear, Charlie,' he commanded his sister, without taking his eyes from Laura's flushed and angry face. 'Laura and I are about ready for a little discussion.'

'We are not ready for anything of the sort,' Laura contradicted stridently as her fury exploded. 'Please stay, Charlotte; I may need you to interpret that fact for your brother.'

Charlotte bit her lip, keeping her face straight, but it was obvious from her dancing eyes that she was smiling. 'This seems to be a love-hate thing.' She shot a mock-contrite look at Laura. 'Forgive me if I don't stay around to see who wins.'

'Charlotte!' Laura cried, outraged as the girl turned to leave.

Mike's sister paused, and shot them both a look of fond exasperation. 'Isn't it time you two stopped fooling about? You obviously adore one another.'

Laura stared after her retreating form, open-mouthed at such treachery, and Mike took advantage of the fact to cover her parted lips with his own. He kissed her passionately... furiously... the fullness of his mouth devouring her sweetness, intent, it seemed, on captivating her very soul. In the first few seconds, filled with outrage, Laura might have struggled free, but, as he continued to hold her in a grip of molten hot steel, his kiss endlessly deepening, outrage and resistance melted irretrievably away.

'Well,' he said at last, having kissed her breathless, 'why don't you?'

'Why don't I what?' Laura gasped, still trying to come back down to earth.

'Marry me!'

Laura stared at him, her breast rising and falling erratically, her head still spinning from the passion he had aroused.

'But how could I?'

'Very easily.' His eyes met hers with sudden intensity. 'If you wanted to. Do you?'

She shook her head to try to clear it. 'But you're engaged to be married, aren't you? To someone else.'

'Whatever gave you that idea?' His mouth curved wryly, making her suddenly angry.

'You did, and you know it. That first day, when you came to the flat to discuss Gladstone House, you told me you wanted the house decorated and furnished to suit a family, since you were thinking of getting married.'

He nodded. 'That's true. But did I mention the name of any specific woman?'

'No,' Laura conceded unwillingly. 'But then, why should you? It was none of my business.'

He kissed the tip of her nose, making her whole body tingle. 'You're wrong. It was very much your business.' He grinned. 'When I arrived at your door, I had no idea who I might marry. Five minutes later, I was certain who my bride would be. The living fulfilment of my dreams.'

Laura pulled herself back as he seemed about to draw her close again. 'You may have time for riddles,' she said tightly. 'I'm afraid I don't.'

'Pity.' He seemed entranced by the angry sparks flying from her eyes. 'They can be a lot of fun.' He put his mouth briefly over hers as she was about to give an angry retort, silencing her effectively. 'It was you, you little idiot,' he murmured against her lips, and then lifted his head to look into her eyes. 'I thought you'd have realised that long ago. It seemed to me to be painfully obvious.'

'You mean...' Laura stared at him disbelievingly '...you were planning to marry me right from the start?' She shook her head.

He nodded. 'From the first moment I set eyes on you...at the college.'

'But that's impossible!'

He laughed. 'Not so impossible. You mustn't underrate yourself.'

She said irritably, 'It's not a question of that. You couldn't possibly have known you wanted to marry me then. You'd only just met me. You couldn't decide that quickly.'

'But I did.' He shook his head at her. 'Two years ago, I saw a beautiful face in a sea of others. A woman with lovely bruised eyes looking intently at me, listening to every word I spoke, but seeing nothing of me as a man. An hour and a half seemed to me then a long time to be falling in love. I didn't know I'd spend two long years haunted by a vision of the only woman I'd ever felt I'd like to marry.'

Laura was so stunned that it was long moments before she could speak. 'Do you mean you never married... because of me?'

He gave a deep sigh. 'Yes. But it wasn't a conscious thing. At first I wanted you, as a person, but since that wasn't possible, and time went by, you became an ideal, everything I wanted encompassed in my dream woman. No one else ever measured up.'

'But that's mad!' Laura felt a mixture of awe and exasperation. 'You didn't know anything about me. If you had, you might not even have liked me.'

'I know. I'd just about reached that conclusion myself when you came back into my life.' He laughed a little harshly. 'I bought Gladstone House intending to live in it with the very next woman who came even close to meaning anything to me. I was tired of dreaming; determined to create some reality... a home... a family...'

He faltered, and Laura heard the catch in his voice. It cut deep into her tender heart. She wasn't responsible for his wasted years, she told herself silently; she couldn't have known... but suddenly they'd become her wasted years too.

Then, he laughed. 'You popped up like a genie. I'd bought Gladstone House—rubbed the lamp—and there you were. It was a miracle. My dream girl returned to me.' His brow darkened. 'But it seemed it was too late after all. When you told me you were going to be married, I couldn't believe it. I'd waited for you . . . why couldn't you have done the same for me?' He shrugged. 'Irrational, but what lover is ever rational?'

Laura frowned. 'So you set out deliberately to win me away from Hubert?'

'No. It wasn't like that.' Mike paused, reaching back into his mind. 'No. At first, I accepted it as some kind of malicious act of fate. Life builds you up to knock you down. I wanted to fight it. I made a tentative effort to see you, but when you turned me down again I was ready to bow out. But then, you introduced me to Hubert Laine that night at the party and I knew he was wrong for you. I knew he could never love you the way I did. All that fire and passion would have been wasted on him. It might sound corny, but that's when I decided it was going to be a case of "all's fair in love and war".' He grinned. 'And what a battle it turned out to be. You fought me every step of the way.'

Laura bit her lip. 'I thought you were doing everything out of revenge for my having turned you down that first time, at the college. I just couldn't see any other reason for your being so good to me and Joe...looking after me...making love to me...when you were going to marry someone else.'

By now he was holding her close again, his lips a whisper away from hers.

'You little idiot. I felt sure you understood, especially after I put you right about the fact that I wasn't going to marry Marietta. Who else could it have been . . . but you . . . ?' His lips touched softly against hers, gentle, undemanding, and so tender that it brought her close to tears. He lifted his head to gaze into her welling eyes. 'I love you, Laura. I have done for a long, long time.'

Torn between laughter and tears, she said gruffly, 'Why couldn't you have told me that before? It would have saved us both a lot of heartache.'

He shook his head. 'I couldn't. I wanted you to decide for yourself about marrying Hubert Laine. In the event of your choosing me over him, I didn't want anything to come between us . . . any lingering doubts that might grow to bitter resentments.' He drew her close again, laying her head against his chest, his hand stroking her thick chestnut hair. 'I wanted your love to be as sure as mine.'

'You fool.' Laura gave a shaky laugh. In his arms like this, with her head lowered where he couldn't see the flush that rose to her cheeks, the stars in her eyes, she could tell him how she felt. 'I was mad about you from the moment I saw you standing on my doorstep. From the moment you engulfed me in those gorgeous, indecently blue eyes, I was fighting a lost cause. I thought it was obvious.'

'Not obvious enough,' Mike said. 'At least, not to me.'

A great, trembling sigh shuddered through her, and she pressed herself against him, giving silent thanks to whatever deity seemed to be watching over her, offering her this second chance of happiness.

He cupped her chin, bringing her up to face him. 'Tell me, Laura. I want to hear it.'

Looking up at him, she was amazed all over again by the masculine beauty of his face, the depth of his blue eyes, which were uncharacteristically uncertain.

'I love you, Mike.' And then, because her voice shook, she said it again . . . firmly, clearly, joyously. 'Oh, Mike! I love you!' She reached up and, for the first time, kissed him with all the love and wonder and gratitude that filled her heart to overflowing, and his arms closed tightly about her.

'Do you think you could finish Gladstone House before our wedding?'

Laura laughed, feeling the last thread of tension melting inside her. 'I should think so. But actually, I haven't said yes.' She looked up teasingly from beneath lowered lashes. 'If you ask me again, I might.'

'OK. If it's formal you want it, formal you'll get it.' He turned to her with a smile that lit up the whole of his face. 'Shall I go down on one knee, or would you rather I held you?'

She snuggled deeper into his arms. 'What do you think?'

He held her, only keeping a distance between them so that he could see her face. 'Laura, my love, my only love. Will you marry me?'

Her answer was in her tear-brimmed eyes, but she said it anyway. 'Yes. Oh, yes!'

His kiss seemed to last a lifetime. When he at last raised his head, they were both breathless.

Laura giggled light-headedly. 'I wonder how Mother will react to another major shock in one day? Only this morning I told her I was cancelling one wedding, and now I'll be telling her I want to arrange another.

She'll probably throw a tantrum that will last for months!'

Mike laughed. 'And then again, she might be thrilled with the new arrangements.'

'What new arrangements?' Laura asked, with a little frown of suspicion.

Mike laughed again. 'What do you think she will say to a wedding in Paris, with a reception in a very high-class French hotel, and lasting a whole weekend?'

'In La Grande?' Laura was almost beyond speech.

'Of course. It's perfectly habitable. In fact, it's luxurious in a faded kind of way. What do you think?'

'I . . . I don't know.' Everything was going too fast for Laura to absorb it. 'She'd probably think it was vulgar, and refuse to come.'

'You don't know your mother as well as you think you do,' Mike said in a satisfied tone. 'I have it on good authority that she's very taken with the whole idea.'

'Oh?' Laura sat up straight in her seat. 'And what do you mean by that remark?'

There was a gleam of mischief in the brief glance he shot at her. 'I've got an ally in the camp.'

'Father?' Laura narrowed her eyes in sudden understanding. 'What have you two been up to?'

He laughed at her threatening tone. 'Just paving the way. Or should I say scattering rose petals on your way to the altar?'

Laura suddenly remembered her mother's uncharacteristically calm acceptance of her cancellation of her wedding to Hubert, and felt the dawn of understanding. Her mother had already known about this. 'Mike Brady,' she said hollowly, 'I think you'd better tell me what's been going on.'

His expression was wary, and Laura had a dismayed feeling he was preparing to do battle. And, if what she suspected was true, that was just what he would be doing.

'OK,' he agreed. 'Your father was concerned. He didn't like the idea of you marrying Hubert any more than I did.'

'You went to the house?' Laura asked in astonishment.

'No. Your father rang me to say thanks for taking Joe to the zoo, and it just went from there. He asked my intentions, and I told him. But we both agreed that you should have freedom of choice, with no lobbying from either of us.'

Laura opened her mouth, but he put up his hand for silence. 'And before you go off half cocked, remember your father only wants your happiness.'

'And what did you want?' she said, beginning to boil. 'Back-up troops as you cut the ground out from under Hubert's feet?'

'That isn't fair, Laura. I wanted you, but not on any terms. If you'd really wanted to marry Hubert Laine, even if I'd thought you would regret it, which I did, I wouldn't have done a thing to prevent it. I wanted you to come to me voluntarily, because you wanted me—not because the ground, as you say, had been cut from under Laine.'

Laura bit her lip, trying to sort out her true feelings from the confusion of anger and betrayal.

'Is that why you didn't tell me you'd seen Hubert at the hotel with a woman he called his wife?'

He heaved a sigh. 'So he did tell you?'

'Yes. Or, at least, he started to. Something made me realise that it had been his voice I'd heard at the hotel, and I couldn't let him go on. After all, I couldn't honestly blame him for doing something I was doing myself.'

'It wasn't quite the same thing, Laura,' Mike said quietly. 'What happened between us was the result of an accident and our feelings for one another. It wasn't planned as Laine's rendezvous obviously was. And I shouldn't be surprised if it wasn't one of many.'

Laura frowned, recalling Hubert's discomfort at having to cancel their dates, his weekend appointments that were too important to postpone even when she'd had an accident and might have needed him, and silently agreed.

'But you couldn't help giving me a clue,' she stated tautly, the anger she denied feeling at Hubert turning towards Mike. 'It couldn't have been clearer.'

'Yes. I did let my anger get the better of me. It shows I'm human, I suppose.' He grinned ruefully. 'I wasn't proud of myself, but I knew you would only really have understood my meaning when or if he confessed.'

'And if he hadn't, would you have told me?'

He held her gaze steadily. 'No.'

Laura was silent for a long time, trying to straighten out her pride from any real hurt. What hurt most was the disappearance of the calm and positive happiness she'd felt earlier.

'So you had your Paris plan all worked out ages ago?'

'Not ages,' he said. 'But I don't deny it was in my head . . . just in case . . .'

She made a sharp sound of frustrated anger. 'You were pretty sure of yourself, Mike Brady.'

He took her clenched hand in his and began to unwind her fingers gently.

'Not of myself,' he told her. 'Only of my love. I love you and I want you, Laura. To live with me in Gladstone House, to share my life, to bear my children, to prosper or fall, in sickness and in health.' His voice broke, and he whispered, 'But only if you want me the same way, with no regrets, no looking back, no doubts.'

Laura felt the tears cascading down her cheeks. Her heart felt as though it was rending in two. Had she somehow spoiled everything . . . dimmed all the light and sparkle that had been their love? Would Mike ever be able to be certain of her feelings for him? It was unbearable.

'I'll ask you again, Laura,' he said, making her heart pound with renewed hope. 'But this time I want you to be absolutely sure.' He kissed the fingers he'd unravelled, one by one, the warmth of his lips seeming to breathe new supple life into her tense body. 'Will you marry me?'

She looked at his handsome face, his unbelievably blue eyes, wide and open, with no shadows lurking in their depths, and knew she wanted him more than anything she had ever wanted in her life.

'Yes, Mike.' She brought his hand to her lips, pressing them against the firm, warm skin, feeling the resurgence of happiness. It made her shy, and came out in teasing. 'Now, will you give me a kiss?'

His face was alight, shining in a way she knew must match her own. 'A million kisses!' he declared, pulling her into his arms. 'Right! Where were we?'

'Umm. About Cloud Seven,' Laura said. 'Do you think we should try for Cloud Nine?'

'I think we should try for heaven,' he murmured, and kissed her.